200 More Words You Need to Know

Kathy Sammis

User's Guide
to
Walch Reproducible Books

As part of our general effort to provide educational materials which are as practical and economical as possible, we have designated this publication a "reproducible book." The designation means that purchase of the book includes purchase of the right to limited reproduction of all pages on which this symbol appears:

Here is the basic Walch policy: We grant to individual purchasers of this book the right to make sufficient copies of reproducible pages for use by all students of a single teacher. This permission is limited to a single teacher, and does not apply to entire schools or school systems, so institutions purchasing the book should pass the permission on to a single teacher. Copying of the book or its parts for resale is prohibited.

Any questions regarding this policy or requests to purchase further reproduction rights should be addressed to:

Permissions Editor
J. Weston Walch, Publisher
321 Valley Street • P. O. Box 658
Portland, Maine 04104-0658

1 2 3 4 5 6 7 8 9 10

ISBN 0-8251-4253-9

J. Weston Walch, Publisher
P. O. Box 658 • Portland, Maine 04104-0658
www.walch.com

Printed in the United States of America

Contents

To the Teacher

200 More Words You Need to Know is a set of vocabulary activity exercises designed for students with special needs. Like its companion volume, *200 Words You Need to Know,* this book contains two hundred words divided into ten units of twenty words each, grouped into categories. Each unit contains ten reproducible pages with eight different vocabulary exercises to reinforce students' learning. Repetition with variety is the key: Each exercise is different but presents the students with each of the twenty vocabulary words (or about half of them for the Crossword Challenge) to recognize and/or write. Bonus activities on some sheets encourage students to complete longer exercises.

The words themselves are common ones students need to master as part of everyday life—for their own personal needs such as cooking, working with tools, and using a computer, and for engaging in activities and interacting with people beyond their homes. Mastery of these words will boost students' self-image and confidence outside the classroom.

Exercise 1, Word Sense, introduces the unit's vocabulary words with simple definitions; students rewrite each word in the blanks provided. As a bonus, those students who can rewrite the boxed letters at the bottom of the page will discover a sentence related to the word category.

Exercise 2, Fun Fill-ins (two pages), encourages students to write the vocabulary words again in the blanks provided, using context clues and letters provided to choose the correct word for each sentence from the given list. The second page is marked BONUS! to encourage students to continue.

Exercise 3, Hidden Words, presents a simple paragraph containing all the vocabulary words for students to locate, with the words listed above, and then provides students with practice in writing each word.

Exercise 4, Lucky Lists, has students classify the vocabulary words, by subject or by initial letter. You may have students alphabetize the words in each grouping after they have completed the classifying; answers are given in alphabetical order for your convenience should you choose this option. On those sheets classifying by initial letter, you may suggest that students write each letter included in the column at the head of the column—for example, for a column reading "Begins with a letter between *A* and *D*," students could write out the letters *A*, *B*, *C*, and *D* before attempting to classify the vocabulary words in the list.

Exercise 5, Puzzle Time, presents a simple puzzle grid. Students use initial letters and word length to fit each word into its appropriate set of puzzle boxes. When words have the same initial letter and length, a second letter is filled in so students can select the correct word for that set of puzzle boxes. The puzzle contains a lighthearted message related to the word category, reading from top to bottom of the puzzle grid. As a bonus, students are asked to find the "secret silly sentence" in the puzzle and rewrite it at the bottom of the page.

Exercise 6, Daffy Definitions (two pages), reinforces students' knowledge of the meanings of the vocabulary words by asking them to choose the correct definition from three given. The second page is marked BONUS! to encourage students to continue.

Exercise 7, Sentence Sense (two pages), uses context clues to test and reinforce students' knowledge of word meanings by asking students to identify the one correct ending to each sentence from three given. Again, the second page is marked BONUS!

Exercise 8, Crossword Challenge, presents a simple crossword puzzle using approximately half of the unit's vocabulary words. Some letters are already filled in, to encourage students to take on this challenge.

You may make as many copies as you want of each reproducible page, so students can work on each exercise as often as necessary to master it. You will find that the last few units have somewhat more difficult words than the earlier units. Flash cards could help students who are having difficulty with particular words or categories.

To heighten student interest and motivation, an illustrated cover sheet is provided for each unit. To make this set into a series of ten mini-workbooks, reproduce the cover of each unit along with the exercise sheets, and then staple cover and worksheets together. Making the worksheets into booklets keeps exercises organized by category and allows students to keep their completed work for review and display. You may wish to encourage your students to color their workbook covers with colored pencils, markers, or crayons, or have students design their own workbook covers.

Optional Activities: Below is a series of optional activities designed to appeal to varying types of learning modalities, including visual, bodily/kinesthetic, logical/mathematical, musical, and interpersonal. Use some or all of these activities to expand the scope of this book's reproducible activity sheets and to draw in all types of learners.

- Make flash cards of the words in a unit.
  - — Students can use the flash cards independently or with a partner to study all of a unit's words or words/units particular students may be having difficulty with.
  - — Have students (alone or in groups) use the flash cards as manipulatives. Ask students to alphabetize the cards, divide them into categories, or sort them by word length and/or part of speech.
  - — Use the flash cards as appropriate in the other optional activities below.
- Ask musically inclined students, alone or in a group, to use a unit's words in a song. Students should choose a simple, familiar melody. They should use as many unit words as possible, but at least eight to ten. Students could then perform their songs for the class.
- Have students draw or bring in to class pictures of a unit's words. Then play a quiz game involving pairs or groups of students, or the whole class. A partner, a group member, or the teacher shows a picture to the other partner, other groups, or the class for oral or written identification. You could use flash cards for this, with students drawing or attaching a picture to the back of the word side of the card.
- Set up a group or individual scavenger hunt. Give students lists or flash cards of unit words and have them find actual examples of things representing the words in the school and community. Students list the location and give a description of each item found.
- Have students write their own unit word stories like the ones in the Hidden Words activities.
- Have students, alone or in groups, act out one of the Hidden Words stories, or one of the students' own stories.
- Play a game of charades. Divide the class into groups. Give each group the same number of words from a unit (flash cards would work well for this). Have groups, and individuals within groups, take turns acting out a unit's words for other groups.
- Divide students into pairs. One partner says a unit word aloud. The other partner writes it down. Both partners check to see if the word is written correctly. The partners continue through all or part of a unit's words, alternating between being the speaker and being the writer. Have each student keep a list of missed words and study them. You or partners could repeat this exercise after students have had time to study the missed words, checking for increased accuracy.

I hope both you and your students will enjoy working with *200 More Words You Need to Know* and that your students will be encouraged by the successes they experience.

—*Kathy Sammis*

Vocabulary List

UNIT 1: AROUND TOWN WORDS

address
block
bridge
building
business
city
courthouse
crosswalk
grocery store
hardware store
hotel
jail
museum
sign
station
street
taxi
town
traffic light
tunnel

UNIT 2: HOUSEHOLD WORDS

air conditioner
alarm clock
cabinet
carpet
ceiling
cellar
curtains
electricity
entrance
exterior
fire escape
furniture
hallway
interior
porch
roof
shelf
staircase
telephone
window

UNIT 3: PEOPLE WORDS

adult
beginner
citizen
companion
enemy
friend
guest
immigrant
individual
messenger
neighbor
partner
passenger
person
president
relative
roommate
stranger
volunteer
woman

UNIT 4: EVENT WORDS

adventure
amusement
anniversary
audience
birthday
carnival
celebrate
circus
contest
election
entertain
holiday
invitation
parade
party
performance
picnic
recreation
travel
wedding

UNIT 5: CHILD CARE WORDS

baby-sitter
bib
bottle
crib
day care
diaper
formula
high chair
immunization
infant
nap
nipple
nurse
nursery
pacifier
playpen
preschool
stroller
teething
toddler

UNIT 6: TOOL AND MACHINE WORDS

appliance
drill
furnace
hammer
incinerator
ladder
lawn mower
lock
machine
needle
pliers
pump
saw
scissors
screwdriver
shovel
sprinkler
staple
tool
wrench

Answer Section

UNIT 1: AROUND TOWN WORDS

Exercise 1: Word Sense

The message reads: I take a taxi across town.

Exercise 2: Fun Fill-ins

1. bridge
2. tunnel
3. jail
4. address
5. town
6. hotel
7. sign
8. city
9. street
10. building
11. business
12. courthouse
13. taxi
14. hardware store
15. crosswalk
16. block
17. grocery store
18. museum
19. traffic light
20. station

Exercise 3: Hidden Words

Today I took the train from my town to the city. The train went across a bridge and through a tunnel. At the city train station, I got into a taxi. I gave the driver the address of the business I wanted to go to. As we drove along the street, the taxi driver stopped at each traffic light. She stopped for each person in a crosswalk, too. We passed a big hotel, a brick jail, a courthouse, and a museum. They were all on the same block. A sign on one big building said "Hardware Store." Another sign said "Shop at Chung's Grocery Store."

Exercise 4: Lucky Lists

A–E: address, block, bridge, building, business, city, courthouse, crosswalk

F–J: grocery store, hardware store, hotel, jail

K–P: museum

Q–Z: sign, station, street, taxi, town, traffic light, tunnel

Exercise 5: Puzzle Time

The secret silly sentence is: Why is that taxi in a jail?

				T	O	W	N									
						H	O	T	E	L						
G	R	O	C	E	R	Y	■	S	T	O	R	E				
					S	I	G	N								
				M	U	S	E	U	M							
					S	T	R	E	E	T						
	C	O	U	R	T	H	O	U	S	E						
	H	A	R	D	W	A	R	E	■	S	T	O	R	E		
					S	T	A	T	I	O	N					
				C	I	T	Y									
				T	R	A	F	F	I	C	■	L	I	G	H	T
				T	A	X	I									
			B	U	S	I	N	E	S	S						
				B	U	I	L	D	I	N	G					
				T	U	N	N	E	L							
C	R	O	S	S	W	A	L	K								
						J	A	I	L							
						A	D	D	R	E	S	S				
				B	R	I	D	G	E							
					B	L	O	C	K							
						?										

Exercise 6: Daffy Definitions

1. b	6. a	11. a	16. c
2. a	7. a	12. c	17. b
3. c	8. b	13. b	18. c
4. b	9. c	14. b	19. c
5. c	10. b	15. a	20. a

Exercise 7: Sentence Sense

1. b	6. a	11. a	16. a
2. a	7. c	12. a	17. c
3. c	8. b	13. c	18. b
4. c	9. b	14. b	19. b
5. b	10. c	15. c	20. a

Exercise 8: Crossword Challenge

Across

2. address
3. business
4. tunnel
6. station
7. hotel
8. sign

Down

1. crosswalk
4. town
5. building
6. street

UNIT 2: HOUSEHOLD WORDS

Exercise 1: Word Sense

The message reads: I like to sit on the porch.

Exercise 2: Fun Fill-ins

1. window
2. roof
3. curtains
4. cellar
5. shelf
6. porch
7. carpet
8. entrance
9. furniture
10. ceiling
11. telephone
12. electricity
13. fire escape
14. air conditioner
15. alarm clock
16. hallway
17. staircase
18. interior
19. exterior
20. cabinet

Exercise 3: Hidden Words

Our apartment building has a very nice entrance. An interior door lets you into the hallway. On the left is a staircase that goes down to the cellar. We live upstairs. We have a new carpet in the living room, although our furniture is old. Our air conditioner is in the window of that room. The kitchen has lots of cabinets for plates and food. It also has a shelf for the telephone. My bedroom has new curtains. Next to my bed is my trusty alarm clock. A ceiling fan keeps the bedroom cool. We also have a back porch with a roof over it. From there, we could reach the fire escape in an emergency. But you have to be sure to keep away from the exterior power lines. They bring electricity to the building.

Exercise 4: Lucky Lists

Machines, devices, energy source: air conditioner, alarm clock, electricity, telephone

Furnishings: carpet, curtains, furniture

On the outside of a building: exterior, fire escape, porch, roof

Built into a house: cabinet, ceiling, cellar, entrance, hallway, shelf, staircase, window

Inside of the building: interior

Exercise 5: Puzzle Time

The secret silly sentence is: The roof is in the cellar.

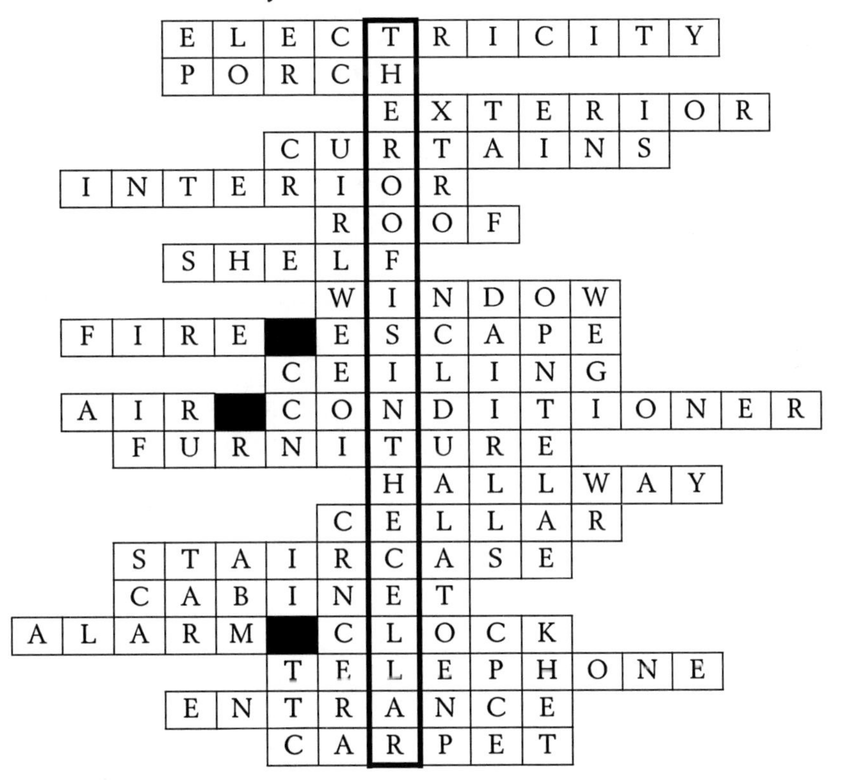

Exercise 6: Daffy Definitions

1. b	6. b	11. a	16. a
2. c	7. c	12. c	17. c
3. a	8. b	13. b	18. b
4. a	9. a	14. b	19. a
5. c	10. c	15. c	20. b

Exercise 7: Sentence Sense

1. b	6. c	11. b	16. c
2. a	7. c	12. c	17. a
3. c	8. a	13. a	18. c
4. b	9. b	14. b	19. c
5. a	10. a	15. b	20. a

Exercise 8: Crossword Challenge

Across	*Down*
5. cellar	1. curtains
8. carpet	2. telephone
9. furniture	3. hallway
10. fire	4. staircase
	6. roof
	7. entrance

UNIT 3: PEOPLE WORDS

Exercise 1: Word Sense

The message reads: Her guest was a relative.

Exercise 2: Fun Fill-ins

1. neighbor	11. immigrant
2. enemy	12. volunteer
3. person	13. roommate
4. adult	14. citizen
5. president	15. passenger
6. friend	16. individual
7. beginner	17. relative
8. stranger	18. companion
9. woman	19. messenger
10. guest	20. partner

Exercise 3: Hidden Words

Many nice people live on my block. Each person who lives here is a friendly individual. No one is a stranger. No one is an enemy. My neighbor is an immigrant from Cuba. He just became a U.S. citizen. He often has a relative stay with him as a guest. My best friend is also my partner. We run the local beauty shop. My roommate works for a messenger service. He is also a volunteer helper at the local adult center. There, he teaches a beginner class in dancing. The old woman next door lives with a nice companion. They often go out on walks. The president of the local taxi fleet lives across the street. She will stop to pick up a passenger on her way to work.

Exercise 4: Lucky Lists

A–E: adult, beginner, citizen, companion, enemy
F–K: friend, guest, immigrant, individual
L–Q: messenger, neighbor, partner, passenger, person, president
R–Z: relative, roommate, stranger, volunteer, woman

Exercise 5: Puzzle Time

The secret silly sentence is: The immigrant is from Mars.

						T							
		N	E	I	G	**H**	B	O	R				
V	O	L	U	N	T	**E**	E	R					
					C	**I**	T	I	Z	E	N		
			E	N	E	**M**	Y						
				C	O	**M**	P	A	N	I	O	N	
		P	R	E	S	**I**	D	E	N	T			
				B	E	**G**	I	N	N	E	R		
				P	E	**R**	S	O	N				
					P	**A**	S	S	E	N	G	E	R
	M	E	S	S	E	**N**	G	E	R				
		R	E	L	A	**T**	I	V	E				
			I	N	D	**I**	V	I	D	U	A	L	
			G	U	E	**S**	T						
						F	R	I	E	N	D		
				S	T	**R**	A	N	G	E	R		
					R	**O**	O	M	M	A	T	E	
				I	M	**M**	I	G	R	A	N	T	
				W	O	**M**	A	N					
						A	D	U	L	T			
P	A	R	T	N	E	**R**							
						S							

Exercise 6: Daffy Definitions

1. c	6. a	11. b	16. a
2. a	7. b	12. c	17. c
3. b	8. a	13. a	18. b
4. b	9. c	14. a	19. c
5. c	10. c	15. b	20. b

Exercise 7: Sentence Sense

1. b	6. a	11. a	16. b
2. a	7. b	12. c	17. c
3. c	8. b	13. b	18. c
4. b	9. c	14. c	19. a
5. c	10. a	15. a	20. b

Exercise 8: Crossword Challenge

Across	*Down*
3. roommate	1. enemy
5. adult	2. person
6. woman	3. relative
8. stranger	4. partner
9. friend	7. neighbor

UNIT 4: EVENT WORDS

Exercise 1: Word Sense

The message reads: We had a birthday picnic.

Exercise 2: Fun Fill-ins

1. contest
2. adventure
3. picnic
4. party
5. celebrate
6. travel
7. birthday
8. wedding
9. parade
10. holiday
11. carnival
12. amusement
13. anniversary
14. audience
15. circus
16. invitation
17. performance
18. election
19. entertain
20. recreation

Exercise 3: Hidden Words

This is going to be a very busy year. We plan to entertain ourselves a lot. It starts with my birthday party. Then we will travel out West. That will be an adventure! Next, we will celebrate our parents' wedding anniversary. In June, we will attend a circus. We will send out invitations for a July 4 picnic. In August, we'll go to a carnival. There, we'll be in a pie-eating contest. We'll also have fun at an amusement park. We will take some time out from our recreation. We will vote on Election Day. My dad plans to march in the Veterans' Day parade. We'll also be part of an audience. That will happen when we attend a performance of holiday music.

Exercise 4: Lucky Lists

A–B: adventure, amusement, anniversary, audience, birthday
C–G: carnival, celebrate, circus, contest, election, entertain
H–L: holiday, invitation
M–Q: parade, party, performance, picnic
R–Z: recreation, travel, wedding

Exercise 5: Puzzle Time

The secret sentence is: Do circus clowns compete?

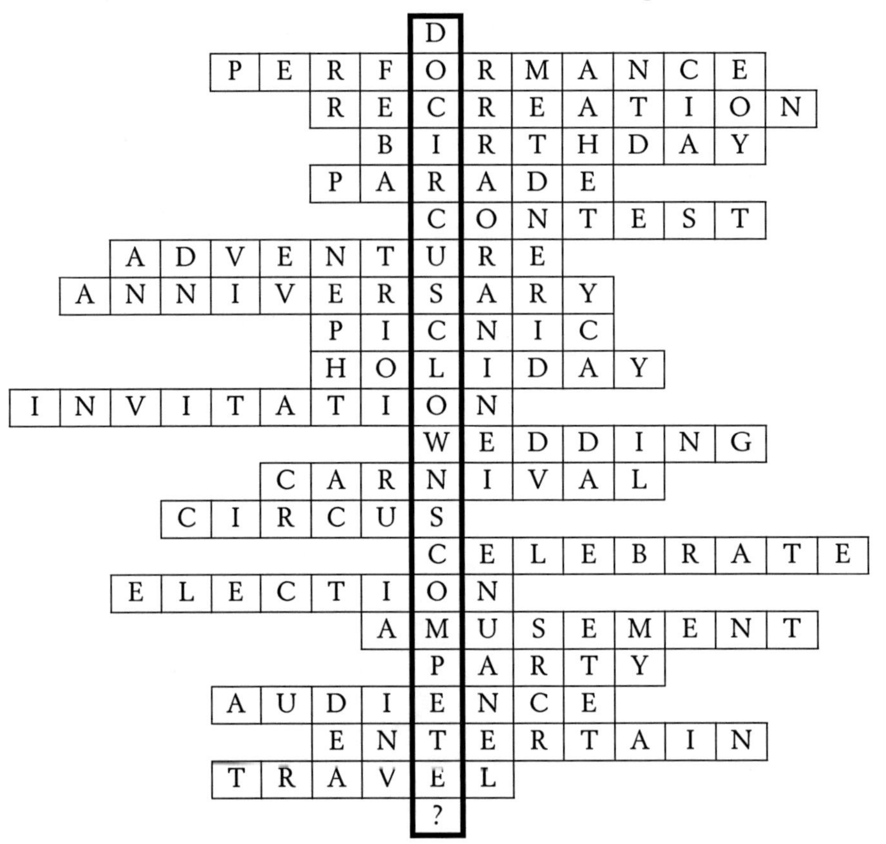

Exercise 6: Daffy Definitions

1. c	6. c	11. b	16. c
2. a	7. b	12. c	17. a
3. b	8. a	13. a	18. c
4. a	9. b	14. a	19. b
5. c	10. b	15. b	20. a

Exercise 7: Sentence Sense

1. a	6. c	11. c	16. b
2. c	7. b	12. a	17. a
3. b	8. c	13. b	18. c
4. b	9. a	14. c	19. c
5. a	10. b	15. a	20. b

Exercise 8: Crossword Challenge

Across
2. celebrate
8. wedding
9. election
10. parade

Down
1. holiday
2. contest
3. birthday
4. travel
5. audience
6. adventure
7. entertain

UNIT 5: CHILD CARE WORDS

Exercise 1: Word Sense

The message reads: Change the baby's diaper.

Exercise 2: Fun Fill-ins

1. bib
2. diaper
3. playpen
4. stroller
5. crib
6. nurse
7. baby-sitter
8. bottle
9. toddler
10. nap
11. nursery
12. high chair
13. infant
14. formula
15. preschool
16. teething
17. pacifier
18. immunization
19. day care
20. nipple

Exercise 3: Hidden Words

Some parents take their baby to day care. Others send their young child to preschool. At home, parents hire a baby-sitter. Here are some tips on being a good baby-sitter. You must know how to take care of an infant and a toddler. You nurse a baby with a bottle. Fill the bottle with formula. Then put on a clean nipple. A toddler can eat in a high chair, wearing a bib. When a baby is tired, bring her to her nursery. Put her down for a nap in her crib. Later, she might enjoy her toys in the playpen. Change the diaper when it's wet. Give a teething baby a cold pacifier to suck on. Or take a fussy child for a walk in the stroller. It's the parents' job to be sure a young child gets all of his immunizations.

Exercise 4: Lucky Lists

Feeding: bib, bottle, formula, nipple, nurse
Equipment and room: crib, diaper, high chair, nursery, pacifier, playpen, stroller (high chair could also be under Feeding)
Child care: baby-sitter, day care, preschool
Young children: infant, toddler
Make baby unhappy: immunization, teething
Baby needs to do: nap

Exercise 5: Puzzle Time

The secret sentence reads: Baby's bibs are in the crib.

				B	A	B	Y	-	S	I	T	T	E	R
F	O	R	M	U	L	A								
						B	I	B						
				D	A	Y	■	C	A	R	E			
						'								
						S	T	R	O	L	L	E	R	
			C	R	I	B								
					N	I	P	P	L	E				
						B	O	T	T	L	E			
			N	U	R	S	E							
					N	A	P							
					P	R	E	S	C	H	O	O	L	
		N	U	R	S	E	R	Y						
			P	A	C	I	F	I	E	R				
		I	M	M	U	N	I	Z	A	T	I	O	N	
	I	N	F	A	N	T								
		T	E	E	T	H	I	N	G					
	P	L	A	Y	P	E	N							
	H	I	G	H	■	C	H	A	I	R				
T	O	D	D	L	E	R								
					D	I	A	P	E	R				
						B								

Exercise 6: Daffy Definitions

1. b	6. a	11. c	16. a
2. a	7. c	12. a	17. a
3. c	8. b	13. b	18. c
4. c	9. b	14. c	19. b
5. b	10. a	15. b	20. c

Exercise 7: Sentence Sense

1. c	6. a	11. a	16. b
2. a	7. c	12. c	17. c
3. c	8. b	13. b	18. c
4. b	9. b	14. c	19. a
5. a	10. c	15. a	20. b

Exercise 8: Crossword Challenge

Across
1. teething
5. nurse
7. stroller
9. bottle
10. pacifier
11. nap

Down
2. toddler
3. infant
4. formula
6. crib
8. playpen

UNIT 6: TOOL AND MACHINE WORDS

Exercise 1: Word Sense

The message reads: Use a drill to make holes.

Exercise 2: Fun Fill-ins

1. ladder
2. machines
3. scissors
4. saw
5. hammer
6. shovel
7. needle
8. lock
9. tools
10. pump
11. sprinkler
12. incinerator
13. pliers
14. screwdriver
15. furnace
16. appliance
17. drill
18. lawn mower
19. wrench
20. staple

Exercise 3: Hidden Words

My job is to take care of this apartment building. I have many hand tools to do repairs. My wrench and pliers help with nuts and bolts. I can secure loose things with my hammer or my staple gun. I use my screwdriver to put in a new lock. My power drill also drives and takes out screws. My needle and scissors come in handy, too. I use them to fix the ripped curtains in the entrance. I also make sure each machine and appliance is working well. I use my ladder to check out the sprinkler system. I clean the furnace often. I also make sure the pump and the incinerator are always in running order. Outdoors, I use my saw to cut up any broken tree branches. I cut the grass with the lawn mower in the summer. In the winter, I shovel snow. My job keeps me very busy!

Exercise 4: Lucky Lists

Machines: pump, appliance, furnace, incinerator, lawn mower, sprinkler

Gripping, turning, fastening, driving tools: hammer, drill, needle, pliers, screwdriver, staple, wrench

Cutting and digging tools: saw, scissors, shovel (optional: drill)

Door: lock

Words for unit words: machine, tool

Climb: ladder

Exercise 5: Puzzle Time

The secret silly sentence reads: We ate lunch on the ladder.

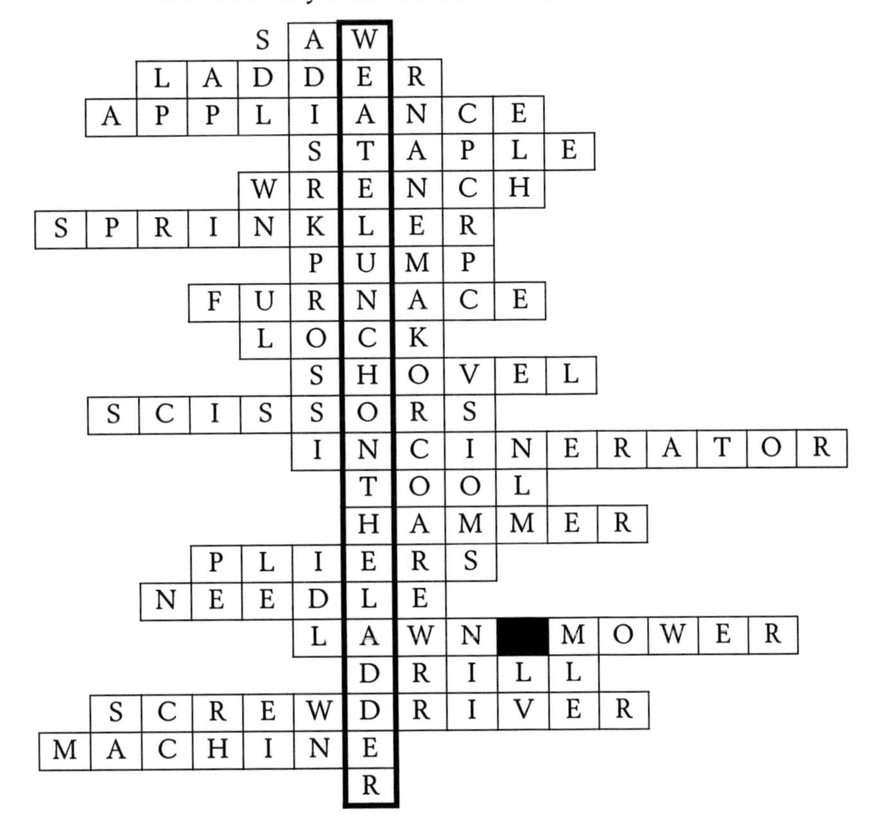

Exercise 6: Daffy Definitions

1. a	6. c	11. b	16. a
2. c	7. b	12. a	17. c
3. b	8. a	13. c	18. b
4. b	9. c	14. c	19. b
5. a	10. b	15. b	20. a

Exercise 7: Sentence Sense

1. b	6. a	11. b	16. b
2. a	7. a	12. c	17. a
3. c	8. c	13. a	18. a
4. b	9. b	14. b	19. c
5. c	10. c	15. c	20. b

Exercise 8: Crossword Challenge

Across

5. screwdriver
8. lock
9. needle
10. sprinkler

Down

1. hammer
2. saw
3. furnace
4. wrench
5. shovel
6. ladder
7. pliers

UNIT 7: COOKING WORDS

Exercise 1: Word Sense

The message reads: I cook dinner in the oven.

Exercise 2: Fun Fill-ins

1. hungry
2. spoon
3. blender
4. knife
5. dinner
6. fork
7. Measure
8. thirsty
9. cookbook
10. oven
11. silverware
12. skillet
13. toaster
14. casserole
15. Nutrition
16. recipe
17. dishwasher
18. saucepan
19. ingredients
20. utensils

Exercise 3: Hidden Words

Today it is my turn to make dinner. I found a new recipe to try in the cookbook. First I measure out all the ingredients. Then I mix them in the blender. Next, I heat the mix in a saucepan and stir with a spoon. Then I pour the mix into a casserole. I bake it in the oven for half an hour. Meanwhile, I cook the meat in a skillet. I also bring the silverware to the table. Next to each plate, I put a knife and a fork. Each thirsty person gets a glass of ice water. Just before I serve the meal, I heat the bread in the toaster. I also put all the used utensils in the dishwasher. Then I call everyone to the table. My meal offers all of us good nutrition. It's tasty, too! I hope we are all hungry!

Exercise 4: Lucky Lists

Cook food in: oven, casserole, saucepan, skillet, toaster

Eat and mix food with: spoon, blender, fork, knife, silverware, utensils

Eating and drinking: dinner, hungry, nutrition, thirsty

Recipes: cookbook, ingredients, measure, recipe

Clean cooking items: dishwasher

Exercise 5: Puzzle Time

The secret silly sentence is: Don't eat soup with a fork.

			B	L	E	N	D	E	R					
							O	V	E	N				
				D	I	N	N	E	R					
							'							
					N	U	T	R	I	T	I	O	N	
		R	E	C	I	P	E							
S	I	L	V	E	R	W	A	R	E					
							T	H	I	R	S	T	Y	
				T	O	A	S	T	E	R				
	C	O	O	K	B	O	O	K						
					S	A	U	C	E	P	A	N		
						S	P	O	O	N				
			D	I	S	H	W	A	S	H	E	R		
		U	T	E	N	S	I	L	S					
	S	K	I	L	L	E	T							
							H	U	N	G	R	Y		
					M	E	A	S	U	R	E			
							F	O	R	K				
	C	A	S	S	E	R	O	L	E					
				I	N	G	R	E	D	I	E	N	T	S
							K	N	I	F	E			

Exercise 6: Daffy Definitions

1. c	6. a	11. b	16. b
2. a	7. c	12. c	17. c
3. b	8. b	13. a	18. a
4. b	9. a	14. a	19. b
5. c	10. b	15. c	20. c

Exercise 7: Sentence Sense

1. b	6. c	11. a	16. a
2. c	7. a	12. c	17. b
3. a	8. b	13. b	18. c
4. b	9. c	14. b	19. b
5. b	10. a	15. c	20. a

Exercise 8: Crossword Challenge

Across	*Down*
3. spoon	1. hungry
7. saucepan	2. skillet
8. toaster	4. oven
9. dinner	5. casserole
10. cookbook	6. blender

UNIT 8: PERSONAL WORDS

Exercise 1: Word Sense

The message reads: A shy child may be lonely.

Exercise 2: Fun Fill-ins

1. lazy
2. greedy
3. popular
4. curious
5. stubborn
6. selfish
7. lonely
8. shy
9. honest
10. cheerful
11. impatient
12. anxious
13. enthusiastic
14. creative
15. sympathetic
16. courageous
17. generous
18. vain
19. ambitious
20. jealous

Exercise 3: Hidden Words

People have many kinds of personal traits. If you are enthusiastic, you are eager to do things. If you're curious, you want to learn about new things. If you're creative, you want to make new things. Are you cheerful and honest? Are you sympathetic and generous? If so, you will be popular. If you're ambitious and not lazy, you'll go far. Being courageous will help you face life's troubles. If you think too much of yourself, you are vain. If you're vain, you may also be selfish and greedy. If you're shy, you may feel lonely. If you are jealous, you will feel anxious about your friends. If you insist on doing things your own way, you are stubborn. If you can't stand any kind of delay, you are impatient. Can you tell which of these traits will bring you the most friends?

Exercise 4: Lucky Lists

A–D: ambitious, anxious, cheerful, courageous, creative, curious
E–K: enthusiastic, generous, greedy, honest, impatient, jealous
L–R: lazy, lonely, popular
S–Z: selfish, shy, stubborn, sympathetic, vain

Exercise 5: Puzzle Time

The secret silly sentence is: The greedy goat ate my oats.

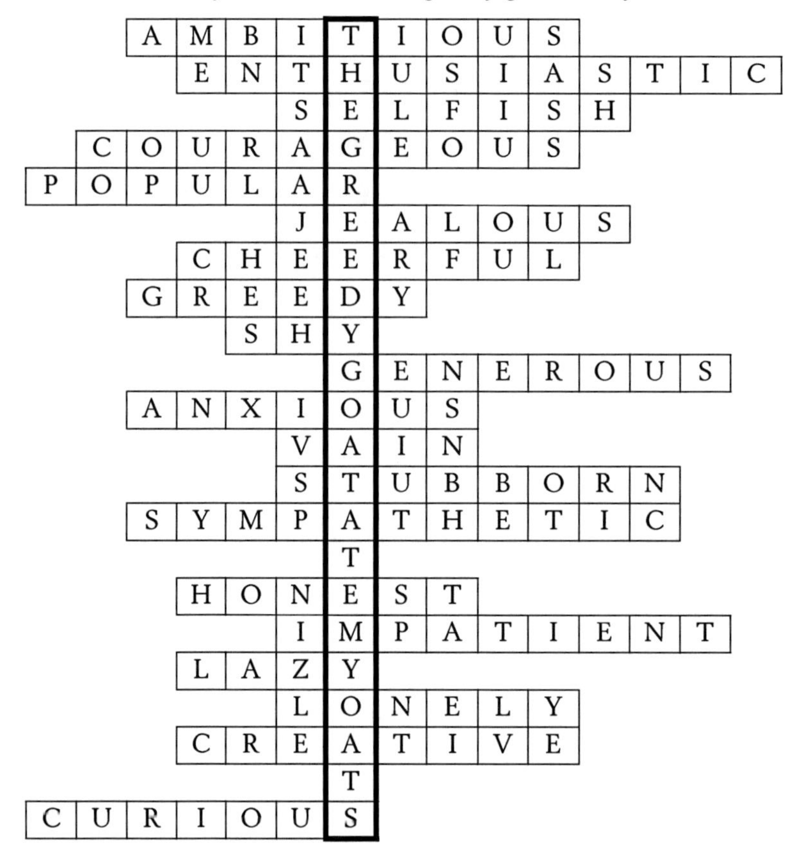

Exercise 6: Daffy Definitions

1. b	6. c	11. a	16. c
2. c	7. b	12. c	17. b
3. a	8. b	13. b	18. a
4. b	9. a	14. b	19. c
5. a	10. c	15. a	20. b

Exercise 7: Sentence Sense

1. c	6. b	11. b	16. a
2. b	7. a	12. a	17. a
3. b	8. c	13. c	18. c
4. a	9. c	14. b	19. b
5. c	10. a	15. c	20. c

Exercise 8: Crossword Challenge

Across	*Down*
5. cheerful	1. generous
6. lonely	2. greedy
8. anxious	3. stubborn
9. creative	4. curious
	7. honest

UNIT 9: COMPUTER WORDS

Exercise 1: Word Sense

The message reads: I send e-mail to my friend.

Exercise 2: Fun Fill-ins

1. mouse	11. workstation
2. keyboard	12. modem
3. laptop	13. hardware
4. cursor	14. software
5. disk	15. on-line
6. memory	16. port
7. drive	17. monitor
8. printer	18. browser
9. e-mail	19. fax
10. computer	20. Internet

Exercise 3: Hidden Words

I work on more than one computer. When I travel, I use my laptop. At work, I have my own computer workstation. My home computer has lots of memory. It also has a color monitor and a large keyboard. I use the mouse to move the cursor around the screen. A color printer is also part of my hardware. It plugs into a port on the back of the computer. The floppy drive lets me save my work on a back-up disk. I can send a fax with the modem. My browser software lets me surf the Internet. While I'm on-line, I can also send e-mail to my friends. I use my computer a lot!

Exercise 4: Lucky Lists

A–D: browser, computer, cursor, disk, drive
E–J: e-mail, fax, hardware, Internet
K–N: keyboard, laptop, memory, modem, monitor, mouse
O–Z: on-line, port, printer, software, workstation

Exercise 5: Puzzle Time

The secret silly sentence is: See my mouse chase my modem!

					D	I	S	K						
S	O	F	T	W	A	R	E							
							E							
							M	O	U	S	E			
					K	E	Y	B	O	A	R	D		
					E	-	M	A	I	L				
			L	A	P	T	O	P						
						C	U	R	S	O	R			
			W	O	R	K	S	T	A	T	I	O	N	
		P	R	I	N	T	E	R						
							C							
							H	A	R	D	W	A	R	E
						F	A	X						
			B	R	O	W	S	E	R					
	O	N	-	L	I	N	E							
					C	O	M	P	U	T	E	R		
		M	E	M	O	R	Y							
							M	O	N	I	T	O	R	
						P	O	R	T					
							D	R	I	V	E			
				I	N	T	E	R	N	E	T			
			M	O	D	E	M							
							!							

Exercise 6: Daffy Definitions

1. a	6. b	11. b	16. a
2. c	7. c	12. a	17. a
3. b	8. a	13. c	18. c
4. b	9. c	14. b	19. b
5. a	10. b	15. c	20. c

Exercise 7: Sentence Sense

1. a	6. c	11. c	16. a
2. b	7. b	12. b	17. b
3. b	8. a	13. b	18. c
4. c	9. c	14. a	19. c
5. a	10. b	15. c	20. a

Exercise 8: Crossword Challenge

Across	*Down*
5. laptop	1. browser
9. printer	2. monitor
10. software	3. modem
11. computer	4. cursor
	6. port
	7. Internet
	8. hardware

UNIT 10: EDUCATION WORDS

Exercise 1: Word Sense

The message reads: A student needs to study.

Exercise 2: Fun Fill-ins

1. homework
2. student
3. answer
4. study
5. problems
6. practice
7. question
8. quiz
9. example
10. chapter
11. exam
12. dictionary
13. graduate
14. college
15. directions
16. atlas
17. textbook
18. education
19. encyclopedia
20. research

Exercise 3: Hidden Words

I study hard to get a good education. I read each chapter of my textbook with care. I answer each practice question. I do each problem the teacher gives as homework. I make sure to follow the directions on each quiz. I do a lot of research for each report I write. I go to an encyclopedia. I look through an atlas. I use a dictionary for help while I write. I make sure I'm ready for each exam. I think I am an example of a good student. I plan to graduate this year. Then I'll attend college.

Exercise 4: Lucky Lists

A–D: answer, atlas, chapter, college, dictionary, directions
E–I: education, encyclopedia, exam, example, graduate, homework
J–Q: practice, problem, question, quiz
R–Z: research, student, study, textbook

Exercise 5: Puzzle Time

The secret silly sentence is: Is a question the answer?

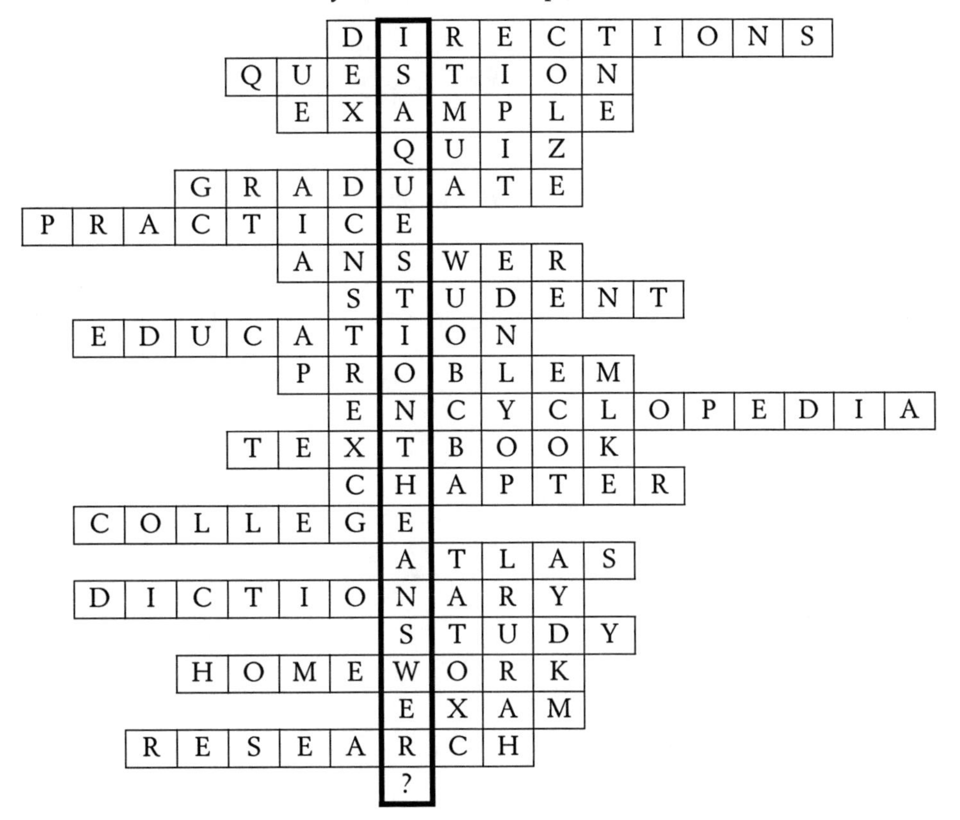

Exercise 6: Daffy Definitions

1. b	6. a	11. a	16. b
2. c	7. c	12. b	17. c
3. c	8. b	13. b	18. a
4. a	9. b	14. a	19. c
5. b	10. a	15. c	20. b

Exercise 7: Sentence Sense

1. a	6. a	11. c	16. b
2. c	7. c	12. a	17. b
3. b	8. b	13. b	18. c
4. c	9. b	14. a	19. a
5. a	10. c	15. c	20. c

Exercise 8: Crossword Challenge

Across

4. college
5. exam
8. student
9. homework

Down

1. chapter
2. problem
3. question
6. answer
7. atlas

Unit 1

AROUND TOWN WORDS

EXERCISE 1

WORD SENSE

Name ______________________________

Date ______________________________

Read each word below and its definition. Rewrite each word in the blanks next to its definition.

1.	building	structure with walls and a roof, like a house or school	_ _ [i] _ _ _ _ _
2.	tunnel	long passage built under ground or water	[t] _ _ _ _ _
3.	jail	place where people who break the law are kept	_ [a] _ _
4.	block	area in a city or town with four streets around it, or one side of such a block	_ _ _ _ [k]
5.	address	exact place where you live or where a business is located	_ _ _ _ [e] _ _
6.	traffic light	signal with colored lights that tells vehicles when to stop or go	_ _ [a] _ _ _ _ / _ _ _ _ _
7.	town	area, smaller than a city, where people live and work	[t] _ _ _
8.	station	regular stopping place for a bus or train line	_ _ [a] _ _ _ _
9.	taxi	car that people hire to take them places	_ _ [x] _
10.	business	activity set up to make money by buying and selling	_ _ _ [i] _ _ _ _
11.	hardware store	place that sells articles to make and fix things	_ [a] _ _ _ _ _ _ / _ _ _ _ _
12.	city	large area where many people live and work	[c] _ _ _
13.	bridge	structure built across a river, road, or train track	_ [r] _ _ _ _
14.	hotel	building with many rooms that people pay to stay in	_ [o] _ _ _
15.	courthouse	place where law cases are heard	_ _ _ _ _ _ _ _ [s] _
16.	museum	building where special objects are displayed	_ _ [s] _ _ _
17.	street	public way used by vehicles (cars, bikes, trucks, etc.)	_ _ _ _ _ [t]
18.	grocery store	place that sells food and household supplies	_ _ [o] _ _ _ _ / _ _ _ _ _
19.	crosswalk	marked path for people walking across a road	_ _ _ _ _ [w] _ _ _
20.	sign	board with words on it that gives information	_ _ _ [n]

BONUS! The boxed letters spell out a sentence. What does it say? (Write it out here if you want to:)

____

Exercise 2
Fun Fill-ins

Name ______________________________

Date ______________________________

Each sentence below has a word (or two words together) missing. Fill in each blank with a word that makes sense from the list at the top of this page. Check off each word in the list as you use it.

sign	tunnel	building
address	bridge	hotel
city	street	jail
	town	

1. On Sunday, we drove our car across the _ r _ _ g _ over the river.
2. On Monday, we drove our car through the _ _ _ n _ l under the river.
3. People who break the law may be locked up in a _ a _ _.
4. My sister's _ d _ _ _ s _ is 355 Main Street.
5. My grandmother lives in a small _ _ w _ out in the country.
6. When Keshawn visited New York City, he stayed in a _ o _ _ _ for two nights.
7. Can you read the words on that road _ _ g _?
8. A big _ i _ _ is full of many people, cars, and buildings.
9. Carlota crossed the busy _ _ r _ e _ with great care.
10. The b _ _ _ d _ _ _ that we live in is five stories tall.

EXERCISE 2 *(continued)*

FUN FILL-INS

Name ______________________________

Date ______________________________

(BONUS! Continue to fill in the blanks from the word list at the top of this page.)

traffic light	block	courthouse
grocery store	business	crosswalk
hardware store	museum	station
	taxi	

11. Jenna decided to open her own computer repair b _ _ _ n _ _ s.
12. You can pay your parking fine at the _ _ u r _ _ o _ s _.
13. Selim takes a _ _ x _ to get home from work when it rains.
14. Sasha stopped at the h _ _ _ w _ _ _   _ _ o _ _ to buy a hammer and nails.
15. Always cross the street at a well-marked c _ _ _ s w _ _ _.
16. All the neighbors had a big _ _ _ c _ party last weekend.
17. Rafael walked to the g _ _ c _ _ _   _ t _ _ e to get some milk and bread.
18. Our class went to the art _ u _ _ _ m to see the show of modern paintings.
19. You must stop your car when the t _ _ f _ _ _   _ _ g _ _ is red.
20. Meet me at the train _ _ a t _ _ _ at nine o'clock.

EXERCISE 3
HIDDEN WORDS

Name ______________________

Date ______________________

Read the following story. Draw a line under each word from the list below when you first find the word in the story. Check off each word in the list as you find it. The first one is done as an example.

sign	traffic light	bridge	building
address	grocery store	tunnel	hotel
city	hardware store	street	museum
✔ town	crosswalk	station	jail
taxi	courthouse	block	business

Today I took the train from my town to the city. The train went across a bridge and through a tunnel. At the city train station, I got into a taxi. I gave the driver the address of the business I wanted to go to. As we drove along the street, the taxi driver stopped at each traffic light. She stopped for each person in a crosswalk, too. We passed a big hotel, a brick jail, a courthouse, and a museum. They were all on the same block. A sign on one big building said "Hardware Store." Another sign said "Shop at Chung's Grocery Store."

Now write each word you marked in the story on the lines below.

town ____________ ____________ ____________

____________ ____________ ____________

____________ ____________ ____________

____________ ____________ ____________

____________ ____________ ____________

____________ ____________ ____________

____________ ____________

EXERCISE 4
LUCKY LISTS

Name ______________________

Date ______________________

Each word in the list at the top of this page belongs in one of the categories listed below. Write each word under the category it belongs to. The first one in two columns is done for you. Check off each word in the list as you use it.

✔ sign	taxi	crosswalk	street	hotel
✔ address	traffic light	courthouse	station	museum
city	grocery store	bridge	block	jail
town	hardware store	tunnel	building	business

Begins with a letter between *A* and *E*

address
____
____
____
____
____
____
____

Begins with a letter between *K* and *P*

____

Begins with a letter between *F* and *J*

____
____
____
____

Begins with a letter between Q and *Z*

sign
____
____
____
____
____
____

EXERCISE 5

PUZZLE TIME

Name ______________________________

Date ______________________________

Fill in the boxes in the puzzle with words that fit from the word list at the top of this page. Check the words off in the list as you use them. The first letter (and sometimes another letter) of each word is given. The first word is done as an example.

sign	traffic light	bridge	building	taxi
address	grocery store	tunnel	courthouse	hotel
city	hardware store	street	museum	block
✔ town	crosswalk	station	business	jail

BONUS! The puzzle has a secret silly sentence. It reads from the top of the puzzle down. Write the puzzle's secret silly sentence here:

____

EXERCISE 6
DAFFY DEFINITIONS

Name ______________________________

Date ______________________________

Choose the correct definition for each word. Circle the letter in front of the definition you choose.

1. street
   (a) crooked
   (b) road
   (c) cold rain

2. sign
   (a) written words on a board
   (b) highway map
   (c) movie

3. block
   (a) a dark color
   (b) small shop
   (c) small part of a city

4. city
   (a) village
   (b) very large town
   (c) furry animal

5. address
   (a) party clothes
   (b) newspaper
   (c) exact place where a person lives

6. town
   (a) local area smaller than a city
   (b) cloth for drying
   (c) loud noise

7. bridge
   (a) structure across a river
   (b) radio tower
   (c) toll-free highway

8. traffic light
   (a) desk lamp
   (b) device that tells cars to stop and go
   (c) streak of light in the night sky

9. museum
   (a) sports park
   (b) marching band
   (c) building where works of art are shown

10. hotel
   (a) hospital
   (b) place to stay overnight
   (c) place where you can borrow books

EXERCISE 6 *(continued)*
DAFFY DEFINITIONS

Name ______________________

Date ______________________

(BONUS! Continue to choose the correct definition for each word.)

11. tunnel
    (a) roadway under a hill
    (b) roadway over a river
    (c) musical instrument

12. jail
    (a) vacation resort
    (b) purple fruit
    (c) place where lawbreakers are locked up

13. business
    (a) overcoat
    (b) buying and selling activity
    (c) nosy neighbor

14. grocery store
    (a) place to buy shoes
    (b) place to buy food
    (c) place to buy pets

15. hardware store
    (a) place to buy tools
    (b) place to buy food
    (c) place to buy CDs and videos

16. courthouse
    (a) place that shows movies
    (b) two-family home
    (c) place where a judge rules on legal cases

17. building
    (a) flower that hasn't opened yet
    (b) structure, like a house or a school
    (c) farm field

18. station
    (a) small country
    (b) tasty piece of beef
    (c) place where a train stops

19. taxi
    (a) striped jungle animal
    (b) nagging itch
    (c) auto that takes people places for a fee

20. crosswalk
    (a) marked lane where you walk across a street
    (b) lane in a road for fast trucks
    (c) walking stick shaped like a cross

EXERCISE 7
SENTENCE SENSE

Name ________________________________

Date ________________________________

Choose an ending that makes sense for each sentence. Circle the letter in front of the ending you choose. The vocabulary word (or words) in each sentence is underlined.

1. I live on a street that is
   (a) a wonderful vegetable garden.
   (b) paved and well lighted.
   (c) my baby-sitter.
2. The sign over the store
   (a) read "Flora's Flower Shop."
   (b) smiled and said thank you.
   (c) is fun to swim in.
3. My address is
   (a) my grandmother.
   (b) very well dressed.
   (c) 230 High Street.
4. I like the city because
   (a) only a few people live there.
   (b) it is a good cook.
   (c) it is full of people and things to do.
5. Felipe lives on a city block that
   (a) is five miles wide.
   (b) has six buildings on each side.
   (c) is ten miles long.
6. When the traffic light is red, you need to
   (a) stop.
   (b) drive on ahead.
   (c) call for help.
7. Take the tunnel
   (a) over the highway.
   (b) across the ocean.
   (c) under the city streets.
8. Use the bridge to
   (a) clean your teeth.
   (b) drive over the freeway.
   (c) start the fire.
9. My town is
   (a) a parking lot.
   (b) quite small.
   (c) a big city.
10. Aunt Samantha runs a business that
    (a) stands on its head.
    (b) studies hard.
    (c) sells TVs and VCRs.

EXERCISE 7 *(continued)*

Name ______________________

SENTENCE SENSE

Date ______________________

(BONUS! Continue to choose the correct ending for each sentence.)

11. I went to the grocery store to
    (a) buy some fruit and cheese.
    (b) go on vacation.
    (c) sleep overnight.
12. At his hardware store, Luis sells
    (a) ladders and lawn mowers.
    (b) sheets and towels.
    (c) milk and juice.
13. Al Capone went to jail because he
    (a) skipped school.
    (b) loved his mother.
    (c) broke the law.
14. This hotel has
    (a) babies to adopt.
    (b) large rooms with big beds.
    (c) a bad head cold.
15. Our class went to the science museum to see
    (a) a dance contest.
    (b) the school gym.
    (c) a show about stars and planets.
16. Sheena went to the courthouse to
    (a) get her legal papers.
    (b) buy ice cream.
    (c) plant her garden.
17. The Empire State Building in New York City is
    (a) a good dancer.
    (b) angry and mean.
    (c) very, very tall.
18. Jamal hurried to the station to
    (a) scold it.
    (b) catch the train.
    (c) see the animals there.
19. Let's take a taxi to
    (a) the moon.
    (b) the theater.
    (c) China.
20. Use the crosswalk to
    (a) walk across the street.
    (b) brush your hair.
    (c) heat up the soup.

EXERCISE 8
CROSSWORD CHALLENGE

Name ______________________________

Date ______________________________

Use the numbered clues to fill in the crossword grid. Some of the letters have been filled in already.

Across

2. Exact place where you live
3. Money-making activity
4. Long underground passage
6. Place where a train stops
7. Building with many bedrooms
8. Board with words on it

Down

1. Marked path across a road
4. Area where people live and work
5. Word for a house or school
6. Public way for cars

Unit 2

Household Words

EXERCISE 1

WORD SENSE

Name ______________________________

Date ______________________________

Read each word below and its definition. Rewrite each word in the blanks next to its definition.

1.	cabinet	piece of furniture with shelves, drawers, and doors	_ _ _ [i] _ _ _
2.	ceiling	inside covering above a room	_ _ _ [l] _ _ _
3.	furniture	movable objects like tables and chairs used in a home or office	_ _ _ _ [i] _ _ _ _
4.	alarm clock	device that sounds a signal at a set time	_ _ _ _ _ _ _ _ _ [k]
5.	cellar	part of a building that is below ground	_ [e] _ _ _ _
6.	staircase	set of steps, railing, and support framework	_ [t] _ _ _ _ _ _ _
7.	air conditioner	machine that cools and cleans air	_ _ _ _ [o] _ _ _ _ _ _ _ _ _
8.	shelf	piece of metal or wood attached to a wall to hold things	[s] _ _ _ _
9.	exterior	outer part of a building	_ _ _ _ _ [i] _ _
10.	interior	inner part of a building	_ _ [t] _ _ _ _ _
11.	roof	top covering of a building	_ [o] _ _
12.	entrance	place through which you enter a building	_ _ _ _ _ [n] _ _
13.	electricity	form of energy that runs motors and produces light	_ _ _ _ [t] _ _ _ _ _ _
14.	hallway	passageway into which rooms open	[h] _ _ _ _ _ _
15.	carpet	fabric covering for a floor	_ _ _ _ [e] _
16.	telephone	machine used to send sound or speech over a distance	_ _ _ _ [p] _ _ _ _
17.	window	wall opening that lets in air and light	_ _ _ _ [o] _
18.	fire escape	metal stairway on the outside of a building	_ _ [r] _ _ _ _ _ _ _
19.	curtains	pieces of cloth hung across a window or door opening	[c] _ _ _ _ _ _ _
20.	porch	roofed area built onto a house	_ _ _ _ [h]

BONUS! The boxed letters spell out a sentence. What does it say? (Write it out here if you want to:)

____

EXERCISE 2
FUN FILL-INS

Name ________________________________

Date ________________________________

Each sentence below has a word (or two words together) missing. Fill in each blank with a word that makes sense from the list at the top of this page. Check off each word in the list as you use it.

shelf	furniture	ceiling
cellar	entrance	carpet
roof	curtains	porch
	window	

1. Open the _ _ _ d _ _ to let some fresh air in.
2. When it rains, our old _ _ _ f leaks.
3. Close the _ u _ _ _ i _ _ to keep your bedroom private.
4. Our washing machine is down in the _ _ l _ _ _.
5. Keisha keeps her books on the _ h _ _ _ in her bedroom.
6. On a hot summer night, I like to sleep out on our screen _ _ r _ _.
7. We covered up the old floor with a nice new _ a _ _ _ _.
8. The _ n _ _ a _ _ _ to our apartment building is always locked.
9. The _ _ r _ _ t _ _ _ store sells tables, chairs, and sofas.
10. When the roof leaks, rain drips through the c _ _ _ i _ _.

EXERCISE 2 *(continued)*
FUN FILL-INS

Name ______________________

Date ______________________

(BONUS! Continue to fill in the blanks from the word list at the top of this page.)

air conditioner	electricity	staircase
alarm clock	interior	telephone
fire escape	exterior	hallway
	cabinet	

11. Sofia makes a __ __ l __ __ h __ __ __ call to her mother in Mexico every week.
12. Our toaster and coffee maker run on __ __ __ c __ r __ __ __ __ __.
13. All the smoke alarms went off. So Dave used the __ i __ __ __ __ c __ __ __ to leave the building.
14. On hot summer days, we want our apartment to stay cool. So we turn on the __ __ r __ __ n __ __ t __ __ __ __ __ __.
15. I depend on my a __ __ __ __ __ l __ __ __ to wake me up each day.
16. The doctor's office is down that __ __ __ __ w __ __, on the left.
17. My puppy loves to run up and down the __ __ __ __ r c __ __ __.
18. Kareem bought __ n __ __ __ __ __ __ paint for the bedroom.
19. Star bought __ x __ __ __ __ __ __ paint for the outside walls.
20. I keep my shaving cream and razor in the bathroom __ __ b __ __ __ __.

EXERCISE 3
HIDDEN WORDS

Name ______________________

Date ______________________

Read the following story. Draw a line under each word from the list below when you first find the word in the story. Check off each word in the list as you find it. The first one is done as an example.

window	air conditioner	telephone	cellar	carpet
roof	alarm clock	staircase	interior	ceiling
shelf	fire escape	✔entrance	exterior	furniture
porch	electricity	curtains	cabinets	hallway

Our apartment building has a very nice entrance. An interior door lets you into the hallway. On the left is a staircase that goes down to the cellar. We live upstairs. We have a new carpet in the living room, although our furniture is old. Our air conditioner is in the window of that room. The kitchen has lots of cabinets for plates and food. It also has a shelf for the telephone. My bedroom has new curtains. Next to my bed is my trusty alarm clock. A ceiling fan keeps the bedroom cool. We also have a back porch with a roof over it. From there, we could reach the fire escape in an emergency. But you have to be sure to keep away from the exterior power lines. They bring electricity to the building.

Now write each word you marked in the story on the lines below.

entrance	______________	______________
______________	______________	______________
______________	______________	______________
______________	______________	______________
______________	______________	______________
______________	______________	______________
______________	______________	

EXERCISE 4
LUCKY LISTS

Name ______________________________

Date ______________________________

Each word in the list at the top of this page belongs in one of the categories listed below. Write each word under the category it belongs to. The first one in two columns is done as an example. Check off each word in the list as you use it.

✔ window	✔ air conditioner	telephone	cellar	carpet
roof	alarm clock	staircase	interior	ceiling
shelf	fire escape	entrance	exterior	furniture
porch	electricity	curtains	cabinets	hallway

Machines, devices, and energy source in a home

air conditioner

____

____

____

Furnishings in a home

____

____

____

Things on the outside of a building

____

____

____

____

Things built into a house

window

____

____

____

____

____

____

The inside of the building itself

____

EXERCISE 5
PUZZLE TIME

Name ______________________________

Date ______________________________

Fill in the boxes in the puzzle with words that fit from the word list at the top of this page. Check the words off in the list as you use them. The first letter (and sometimes another letter) of each word is given. The first word is done as an example.

window	air conditioner	telephone	cellar	carpet
roof	alarm clock	staircase	interior	ceiling
shelf	fire escape	entrance	exterior	furniture
porch	✔electricity	curtains	cabinet	hallway

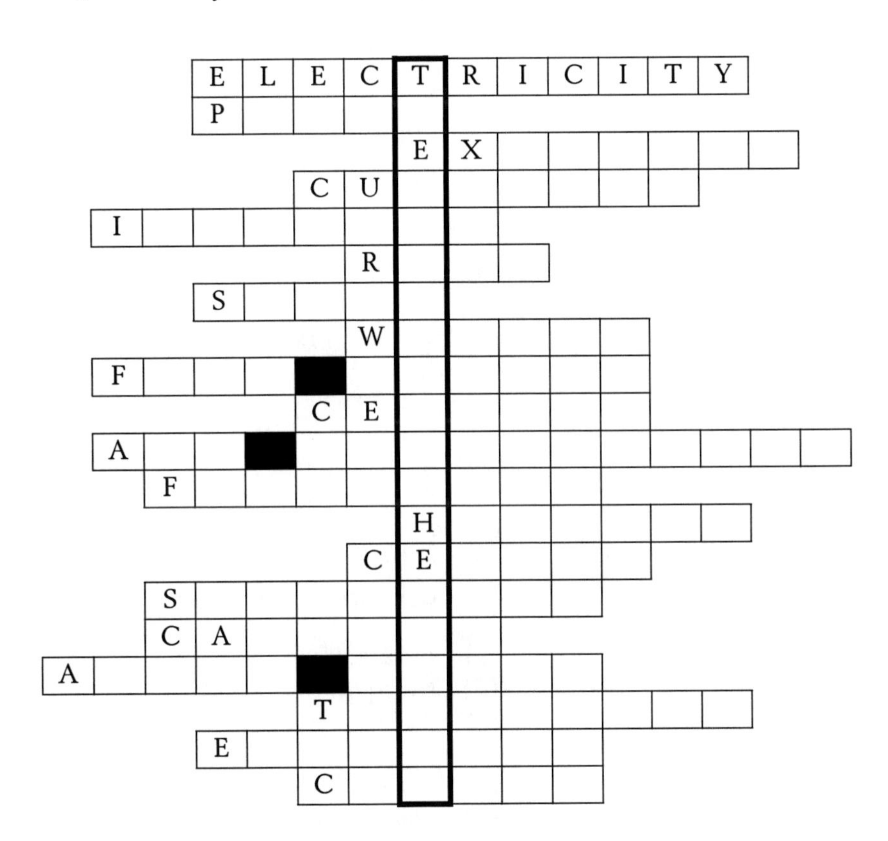

BONUS! The puzzle has a secret silly sentence. It reads from the top of the puzzle down. Write the puzzle's secret silly sentence here:

____

EXERCISE 6
DAFFY DEFINITIONS

Name ______________________________

Date ______________________________

Choose the correct definition for each word. Circle the letter in front of the definition you choose.

1. window
   (a) basement
   (b) wall opening
   (c) woman without a husband

2. roof
   (a) underground plant part
   (b) loud cheer
   (c) top of a building

3. curtains
   (a) window coverings
   (b) fur robes
   (c) dark clouds

4. cellar
   (a) basement
   (b) attic
   (c) wireless phone

5. shelf
   (a) person
   (b) book of recipes
   (c) board on wall that holds things

6. porch
   (a) farm animal
   (b) outside part of a house
   (c) tall, formal hat

7. carpet
   (a) ceiling covering
   (b) fruit jam
   (c) floor covering

8. entrance
   (a) place where you leave
   (b) place where you enter
   (c) dead end

9. furniture
   (a) tables and chairs
   (b) apples and oranges
   (c) puppies and kittens

10. ceiling
   (a) light, thin fabric
   (b) circus animal
   (c) top of a room

EXERCISE 6 *(continued)*

Name ______________________________

DAFFY DEFINITIONS

Date ______________________________

(BONUS! Continue to choose the correct definition for each word.)

11. fire escape
    (a) metal outside stairway
    (b) smoke alarm
    (c) truck for putting out fires

12. electricity
    (a) gloomy feeling
    (b) holiday party
    (c) form of energy

13. telephone
    (a) movie-viewing machine
    (b) calling device
    (c) sleepy trance

14. air conditioner
    (a) machine to heat air
    (b) machine to cool air
    (c) violent windstorm

15. alarm clock
    (a) device that warns about smoke and fire
    (b) device that checks your pulse
    (c) device that wakes you up

16. hallway
    (a) corridor
    (b) concert hall
    (c) order to halt

17. cabinet
    (a) inground pool
    (b) hair net
    (c) place to store things

18. staircase
    (a) carton of blocks
    (b) set of steps
    (c) stepladder

19. interior
    (a) inner part
    (b) outer part
    (c) skin

20. exterior
    (a) inner part
    (b) outer part
    (c) X-ray machine

EXERCISE 7

SENTENCE SENSE

Name ______________________________

Date ______________________________

Choose an ending that makes sense for each sentence. Circle the letter in front of the ending you choose. The vocabulary word (or words) in each sentence is underlined.

1. The roof of my house
   (a) is covered in yellow feathers.
   (b) keeps out the rain.
   (c) is under the stairs.
2. Alan bought new curtains
   (a) to hang on the windows.
   (b) to wear to work.
   (c) to plant in the park.
3. I don't like the cellar because it
   (a) growls at me.
   (b) is too hard to chew.
   (c) is dark and spooky.
4. A shelf is a good place to
   (a) take a nap.
   (b) keep cookbooks.
   (c) visit on vacation.
5. Our front porch is
   (a) a nice place to sit.
   (b) very well behaved.
   (c) a muddy swamp.
6. My bedroom window
   (a) won't brush its teeth.
   (b) floats in the air.
   (c) looks out on the street.
7. Linda put a small carpet
   (a) on the ceiling.
   (b) on the baby's head.
   (c) at the foot of the stairs.
8. When you walk through the entrance, you are
   (a) entering the building.
   (b) buying groceries.
   (c) becoming a vegetable.
9. For furniture, Carlos had
   (a) a pair of jeans and a jacket.
   (b) a bed, a sofa, and two chairs.
   (c) a bike and a skateboard.
10. We will put the new ceiling
    (a) over the top of the room.
    (b) on the walls of the room.
    (c) in the garbage disposal.

EXERCISE 7 *(continued)*

SENTENCE SENSE

Name ______________________________

Date ______________________________

(BONUS! Continue to choose the correct ending for each sentence.)

11. I used the telephone to
    (a) make soup.
    (b) call my brother.
    (c) stack the boxes.
12. We need electricity to
    (a) wear clothes.
    (b) sing the national anthem.
    (c) turn the lights on.
13. Matt used the fire escape to
    (a) get out of the burning building.
    (b) tape the movie.
    (c) fly to Florida.
14. Venus turned on the air conditioner because she was
    (a) too cold.
    (b) too hot.
    (c) thirsty and wanted a drink.
15. I rely on my alarm clock to
    (a) put me to sleep.
    (b) wake me up.
    (c) read the newspaper for me.
16. The long hallway took Deon to
    (a) the Land of Oz.
    (b) the top of the fire tower.
    (c) his friend's apartment.
17. You must go up the staircase to
    (a) get to the fourth floor.
    (b) get to the cellar.
    (c) stay where you are.
18. In the interior of the building is the
    (a) roof.
    (b) front porch.
    (c) bathroom.
19. On the exterior of the building is the
    (a) hallway.
    (b) kitchen cabinet.
    (c) fire escape.
20. In the new cabinet, I plan to keep my
    (a) plates and glasses.
    (b) sleeping baby.
    (c) bath water.

EXERCISE 8
CROSSWORD CHALLENGE

Name ______________________

Date ______________________

Use the numbered clues to fill in the crossword grid. Some of the letters have been filled in already.

Across

5. Below-ground part of a building
8. Floor covering
9. Tables, chairs, sofas, etc.
10. ____ escape: a metal outside stairway

Down

1. Cloth you hang on windows
2. Machine that carries your voice over distance
3. Passageway inside a building
4. Set of inside steps
6. Top covering of a building
7. Place where you enter a building

Unit 3

People Words

EXERCISE 1
WORD SENSE

Name ______________________________

Date ______________________________

Read each word below and its definition. Rewrite each word in the blanks next to its definition.

Word	Definition	Blanks
1. neighbor	person who lives next door to or near you	_ _ _ _ [h] _ _ _
2. beginner	person who is starting to do a thing for the first time	_ _ _ _ _ _ [e] _
3. partner	person who runs a business with another person	_ _ [r] _ _ _ _
4. messenger	person who delivers messages	_ _ _ _ _ _ [g] _ _
5. adult	person who is fully grown up	_ _ [u] _ _
6. enemy	person who hates or wishes to harm another person	[e] _ _ _ _
7. person	man, woman, or child; a human being	_ _ _ [s] _ _
8. roommate	person with whom you share a place where you both live	_ _ _ _ _ _ [t] _
9. woman	adult female person	[w] _ _ _ _
10. companion	person who often goes along and does things with someone else	_ _ _ _ [a] _ _ _ _
11. president	person who is the head of an organization or government	_ _ _ [s] _ _ _ _ _
12. stranger	person you don't know at all	_ _ _ [a] _ _ _ _
13. immigrant	person who comes to live in a country in which he or she was not born	_ _ _ _ _ [r] _ _ _
14. friend	person you know and like well	_ _ _ [e] _ _
15. relative	person who belongs to the same family as you do	_ _ [l] _ _ _ _ _
16. passenger	person who travels in a car, train, bus, plane, or boat	_ [a] _ _ _ _ _ _ _
17. citizen	a resident of a city, town, or country; one who is entitled to the rights of a free person	_ _ [t] _ _ _ _
18. individual	single person or thing; single or separate	_ _ _ [i] _ _ _ _ _ _
19. volunteer	person who offers to help and does it without pay	[v] _ _ _ _ _ _ _ _
20. guest	person who is at another person's home for a meal or a visit	_ _ [e] _ _

BONUS! The boxed letters spell out a sentence. What does it say? (Write it out here if you want to:)

____

EXERCISE 2
FUN FILL-INS

Name ______________________________

Date ______________________________

Each sentence below has a word (or two words together) missing. Fill in each blank with a word that makes sense from the list at the top of this page. Check off each word in the list as you use it.

friend	beginner	enemy
person	neighbor	adult
woman	president	guest
	stranger	

1. My next-door _ _ _ g _ b _ _ is my good friend.
2. An _ n _ _ _ will try to hurt you.
3. Who was that _ _ _ _ _ n you were talking to?
4. You must be an _ _ u _ _ to see that movie.
5. Jackie was elected _ r _ _ i _ _ _ _ of her class.
6. Nate and his best _ _ _ e _ _ spend most of their free time with each other.
7. My little sister is a _ _ g _ _ n _ _, just starting to read.
8. The new student was a complete _ t _ _ n _ _ _ to the rest of the class.
9. The _ _ _ a _ wore a long skirt and tall boots.
10. Our aunt was a _ u _ _ _ in our home for two days.

EXERCISE 2 *(continued)*

FUN FILL-INS

Name ______________________________

Date ______________________________

(BONUS! Continue to fill in the blanks from the word list at the top of this page.)

relative	messenger	immigrant
roommate	volunteer	passenger
partner	individual	companion
citizen		

11. Nadia is a recent _ m _ _ _ r _ _ _ from Poland.

12. I work as a _ _ l _ _ t _ _ _ at the soup kitchen twice a week.

13. My _ _ _ m _ _ _ e pays half of the rent on our apartment.

14. Juan just became a United States _ _ _ _ z _ _.

15. Kendra rode along in the car as a p _ _ _ _ n _ _ _.

16. Each child at the birthday party took home an
_ _ d _ _ _ d _ _ _ balloon.

17. My cousin is my favorite r _ _ _ _ _ v _.

18. My dog, though, is my favorite _ o _ _ _ n _ _ _.

19. Matt enjoys his job as a bicycle _ _ _ s _ n _ _ _.

20. My father is my _ _ _ t _ _ _ in our lawn-mowing business.

EXERCISE 3
HIDDEN WORDS

Name ______________________

Date ______________________

Read the following story. Draw a line under each word from the list below when you first find the word in the story. Check off each word in the list as you find it. The first one is done as an example.

friend	neighbor	adult	president	companion
✔ person	beginner	enemy	volunteer	individual
woman	stranger	partner	roommate	immigrant
guest	passenger	citizen	relative	messenger

Many nice people live on my block. Each person who lives here is a friendly individual. No one is a stranger. No one is an enemy. My neighbor is an immigrant from Cuba. He just became a U.S. citizen. He often has a relative stay with him as a guest. My best friend is also my partner. We run the local beauty shop. My roommate works for a messenger service. He is also a volunteer helper at the local adult center. There, he teaches a beginner class in dancing. The old woman next door lives with a nice companion. They often go out on walks. The president of the local taxi fleet lives across the street. She will stop to pick up a passenger on her way to work.

Now write each word you marked in the story on the lines below.

person	______	______
______	______	______
______	______	______
______	______	______
______	______	______
______	______	______
______	______	

EXERCISE 4
LUCKY LISTS

Name ______________________

Date ______________________

Each word in the list at the top of this page belongs in one of the categories listed below. Write each word under the category it belongs to. The first word in two columns is done as an example. Check off each word in the list as you use it.

friend	neighbor	adult	president	companion
✔ person	✔ beginner	enemy	volunteer	individual
woman	stranger	partner	roommate	immigrant
guest	passenger	citizen	relative	messenger

Begins with a letter between *A* and *E*

beginner
____
____
____
____

Begins with a letter between *F* and *K*

____
____
____
____

Begins with a letter between *L* and Q

person
____
____
____
____
____

Begins with a letter between *R* and *Z*

____
____
____
____
____

EXERCISE 5
PUZZLE TIME

Name ____________________________

Date ____________________________

Fill in the boxes in the puzzle with words that fit from the word list at the top of this page. Check the words off in the list as you use them. The first letter (and sometimes another letter) of each word is given. The first word is done as an example.

friend	✔neighbor	adult	president	companion
person	beginner	enemy	volunteer	individual
woman	stranger	partner	roommate	immigrant
guest	passenger	citizen	relative	messenger

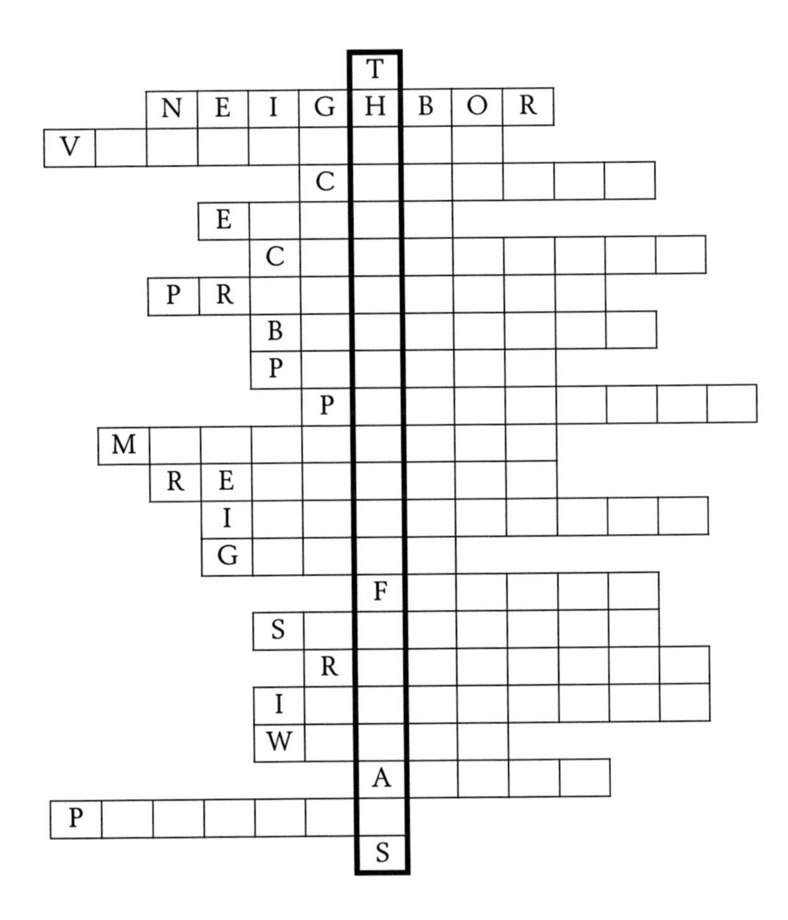

BONUS! The puzzle has a secret silly sentence. It reads from the top of the puzzle down. Write the puzzle's secret silly sentence here:

____

EXERCISE 6
DAFFY DEFINITIONS

Name ______________________________

Date ______________________________

Choose the correct definition for each word. Circle the letter in front of the definition you choose.

1. friend
   (a) complete stranger
   (b) person you don't like at all
   (c) person you know and like well

2. person
   (a) human being
   (b) family pet
   (c) tall tree

3. woman
   (a) adult male person
   (b) adult female person
   (c) baby female

4. neighbor
   (a) person who lives far away
   (b) person who lives next door
   (c) horse that you ride

5. beginner
   (a) person who's an expert
   (b) person who can't sleep
   (c) person who's starting something

6. adult
   (a) fully grown-up person
   (b) early teenager
   (c) boring person

7. guest
   (a) person who guesses at answers
   (b) visitor in your home
   (c) your roommate

8. enemy
   (a) person who's against you
   (b) your best friend
   (c) champion athlete

9. stranger
   (a) person who behaves badly
   (b) person you know and like well
   (c) person you don't know at all

10. passenger
   (a) ticket seller
   (b) person who walks past you
   (c) person who travels in a bus or car

EXERCISE 6 *(continued)*

DAFFY DEFINITIONS

Name ______________________________

Date ______________________________

(BONUS! Continue to choose the correct definition for each word.)

11. president
    (a) junior employee
    (b) head of a company
    (c) brand of toothpaste

12. partner
    (a) person who runs a business alone
    (b) person who likes to party
    (c) one of two people who run a business together

13. citizen
    (a) resident of a town
    (b) tourist
    (c) city worker

14. volunteer
    (a) person who works for no pay
    (b) highly paid worker
    (c) slave laborer

15. roommate
    (a) roof cleaner
    (b) person who lives with you
    (c) waiter or waitress

16. relative
    (a) family member
    (b) person with no family
    (c) person you can rely on

17. companion
    (a) professor
    (b) stranger
    (c) buddy

18. individual
    (a) group of people
    (b) one single person
    (c) couple

19. immigrant
    (a) native-born person of this country
    (b) animal doctor
    (c) person who comes from another country

20. messenger
    (a) person who makes messes
    (b) person who delivers packages
    (c) cafeteria chef

EXERCISE 7
SENTENCE SENSE

Name ______________________________

Date ______________________________

Choose an ending that makes sense for each sentence. Circle the letter in front of the ending you choose. The vocabulary word (or words) in each sentence is underlined.

1. My best friend and I
   (a) hate each other.
   (b) spend every weekend with each other.
   (c) don't know each other.
2. The word for more than one person is
   (a) people.
   (b) women.
   (c) children.
3. The woman who lives upstairs
   (a) is my husband.
   (b) sheds her leaves in the fall.
   (c) sings loudly.
4. To visit his neighbor, Noah
   (a) swims the great lake.
   (b) walks across the yard.
   (c) takes a jet plane.
5. A beginner at playing pool
   (a) always wins.
   (b) gives lessons on how to play.
   (c) doesn't often win.
6. The enemy army
   (a) fought against us.
   (b) fought with us.
   (c) admired and helped us.
7. You should treat a guest in your home
   (a) like a thief.
   (b) like a welcome visitor.
   (c) like an employee.
8. The passenger on the bus
   (a) worked as the bus driver.
   (b) paid a fare to ride.
   (c) ran along beside the bus.
9. The adult trip leader was
   (a) younger than the children.
   (b) just eleven years old.
   (c) older than the children.
10. When the stranger came to town
    (a) no one knew him.
    (b) we were glad to see him again.
    (c) everyone knew him well.

EXERCISE 7 *(continued)*

SENTENCE SENSE

Name ______________________________

Date ______________________________

(BONUS! Continue to choose the correct ending for each sentence.)

11. The president of the United States
    (a) is the head of government.
    (b) has no power.
    (c) must be a teenager.
12. When I work with a partner,
    (a) I work all alone.
    (b) I am lying.
    (c) we work together as a team.
13. A United States citizen
    (a) lives under water.
    (b) can vote in elections.
    (c) has no freedom of speech.
14. Sabrina works as a volunteer because she wants to
    (a) earn a lot of money.
    (b) be selfish.
    (c) help people.
15. The job of our office messenger is to
    (a) deliver notes and packages.
    (b) cook our meals.
    (c) make big messes.
16. Each individual in this class
    (a) is a couple.
    (b) must take the final exam.
    (c) are multiple people.
17. One type of relative is a
    (a) tomato.
    (b) library.
    (c) grandparent.
18. Marcus took a companion with him
    (a) so he would be alone.
    (b) to put in the garbage.
    (c) so he would not be alone.
19. My roommate and I
    (a) share a two-bedroom apartment.
    (b) are toasters.
    (c) live alone in our own homes.
20. My parents were immigrants to the United States. They were born in
    (a) outer space.
    (b) Africa.
    (c) New York.

Exercise 8
Crossword Challenge

Name ____________________

Date ____________________

Use the numbered clues to fill in the crossword grid. Some of the letters have been filled in already.

Across

3. Person you live with
5. Fully grown-up person
6. Adult female person
8. Person you don't know at all
9. Person you know and like well

Down

1. Person who wants to harm you
2. Human being
3. Family member
4. Person you run a business with
7. Person who lives next door

Unit 4

Event Words

Exercise 1
Word Sense

Name ______________________________

Date ______________________________

Read each word below and its definition. Rewrite each word in the blanks next to its definition.

1.	wedding	marriage ceremony and celebration	[w] _ _ _ _ _ _
2.	performance	play, music program, etc.	_ [e] _ _ _ _ _ _ _ _ _
3.	birthday	day you were born	_ _ _ _ [h] _ _ _
4.	carnival	fair or festival with games, rides, and other amusements	_ _ _ _ _ _ [a] _
5.	adventure	exciting or unusual experience	_ [d] _ _ _ _ _ _ _
6.	amusement	something that entertains and makes people pleased and happy	[a] _ _ _ _ _ _ _ _
7.	celebrate	to honor a special day with formal acts and other activities	_ _ _ _ [b] _ _ _ _
8.	circus	show with trained animal acts, feats of daring and skill, and clowns	_ [i] _ _ _ _
9.	travel	to go from one place to another, to make a trip	_ [r] _ _ _ _
10.	contest	game or race that people try to win	_ _ _ _ _ _ [t]
11.	holiday	day when most people don't work or go to school	[h] _ _ _ _ _ _
12.	audience	group of people gathered to see or hear something	_ _ [d] _ _ _ _ _
13.	recreation	something you do to amuse or relax yourself	_ _ _ _ _ [a] _ _ _ _
14.	party	gathering of people to have a good time	_ _ _ _ [y]
15.	parade	public march by a group of people, in honor of a person or event	[p] _ _ _ _ _
16.	invitation	written or spoken request to do something	_ _ _ _ _ _ _ [i] _ _
17.	election	act of choosing by voting	_ _ _ [c] _ _ _ _
18.	anniversary	return each year of a date that marks a special event	_ _ [n] _ _ _ _ _ _ _ _
19.	entertain	to keep someone interested and amused; to have someone as a guest	_ _ _ _ _ _ _ [i] _
20.	picnic	outing with food brought along by the group, eaten outdoors	_ _ _ _ _ [c]

BONUS! The boxed letters spell out a sentence. What does it say? (Write it out here if you want to:)

____

EXERCISE 2
FUN FILL-INS

Name ______________________________

Date ______________________________

Each sentence below has a word missing. Fill in each blank with a word that makes sense from the list at the top of this page. Check off each word in the list as you use it.

party	holiday	parade
birthday	celebrate	contest
picnic	adventure	travel
	wedding	

1. Megan entered a __ o __ __ __ s __ to sell the most raffle tickets.
2. Our camping trip was a great outdoor __ __ v __ __ t __ __ e.
3. The rain ended our __ __ c __ __ __ all of a sudden.
4. Ramon invited ten of his friends to a weekend __ __ __ __ y.
5. The students always c __ __ e __ __ __ __ __ the end of the school year.
6. We plan to __ __ __ v __ __ to Puerto Rico on our vacation.
7. Healy's __ i __ __ h __ __ __ is on May 11.
8. My sister's w __ __ d __ __ __ took place at the local church.
9. Our school band marched and played in the July 4th __ __ __ __ d __.
10. Labor Day is a popular end-of-summer __ __ l __ d __ __.

EXERCISE 2 *(continued)*

FUN FILL-INS

Name ______________________________

Date ______________________________

(BONUS! Continue to fill in the blanks from the word list at the top of this page.)

election	invitation	amusement
carnival	anniversary	entertain
audience	recreation	circus
	performance	

11. We ate cotton candy at the _ a _ _ _ v _ _.

12. We rode a roller-coaster at the _ m _ _ _ m _ _ _ park.

13. Monday was my parents' wedding _ _ n _ v _ _ s _ _ _.
    So I took them out to dinner.

14. The a _ _ _ _ n _ _ clapped and cheered for the band.

15. The _ _ _ c _ _ clowns made everyone laugh.

16. Did you get an _ _ v _ t _ _ i _ _ to Emmett's party?

17. I thought the singer's p _ _ f _ _ _ a _ _ _ was fine.

18. Be sure to vote on _ l _ c _ _ _ _ _ day.

19. We plan to _ _ t _ _ t _ _ _ four guests on Sunday.

20. I love to go fishing. It's fun and cheap _ e c _ _ _ t _ _ _.

EXERCISE 3
HIDDEN WORDS

Name ____________________

Date ____________________

Read the following story. Draw a line under each word from the list below when you first find the word in the story. Check off each word in the list as you find it. The first one is done as an example.

parade	birthday	holiday	✔ entertain	anniversary
party	wedding	travel	celebrate	performance
picnic	election	carnival	recreation	invitations
circus	contest	audience	adventure	amusement

This is going to be a very busy year. We plan to entertain ourselves a lot. It starts with my birthday party. Then we will travel out West. That will be an adventure! Next, we will celebrate our parents' wedding anniversary. In June, we will attend a circus. We will send out invitations for a July 4th picnic. In August, we'll go to a carnival. There, we'll be in a pie-eating contest. We'll also have fun at an amusement park. We will take some time out from our recreation. We will vote on Election Day. My dad plans to march in the Veterans' Day parade. We'll also be part of an audience. That will happen when we attend a performance of holiday music.

Now write each word you marked in the story on the lines below.

entertain

EXERCISE 4
LUCKY LISTS

Name ______________________________

Date ______________________________

Each word in the list at the top of this page belongs in one of the categories listed below. Write each word under the category it belongs to. The first word in two columns is done as an example. Check off each word in the list as you use it.

parade	✔birthday	holiday	entertain	anniversary
party	wedding	travel	celebrate	performance
picnic	election	carnival	recreation	invitation
✔circus	contest	audience	adventure	amusement

Begins with a letter between *A* and *B*

birthday
____
____
____
____

Begins with a letter between C and G

circus
____
____
____
____
____

Begins with a letter between *H* and *L*

____
____

Begins with a letter between *M* and Q

____
____
____
____

Begins with a letter between *R* and *Z*

____
____
____

EXERCISE 5

PUZZLE TIME

Name ______________________________

Date ______________________________

Fill in the boxes in the puzzle with words that fit from the word list at the top of this page. Check the words off in the list as you use them. The first letter (and sometimes another letter) of each word is given. The first word is done as an example.

parade	birthday	holiday	entertain	anniversary
party	wedding	travel	celebrate	✔ performance
picnic	election	carnival	recreation	invitation
circus	contest	audience	adventure	amusement

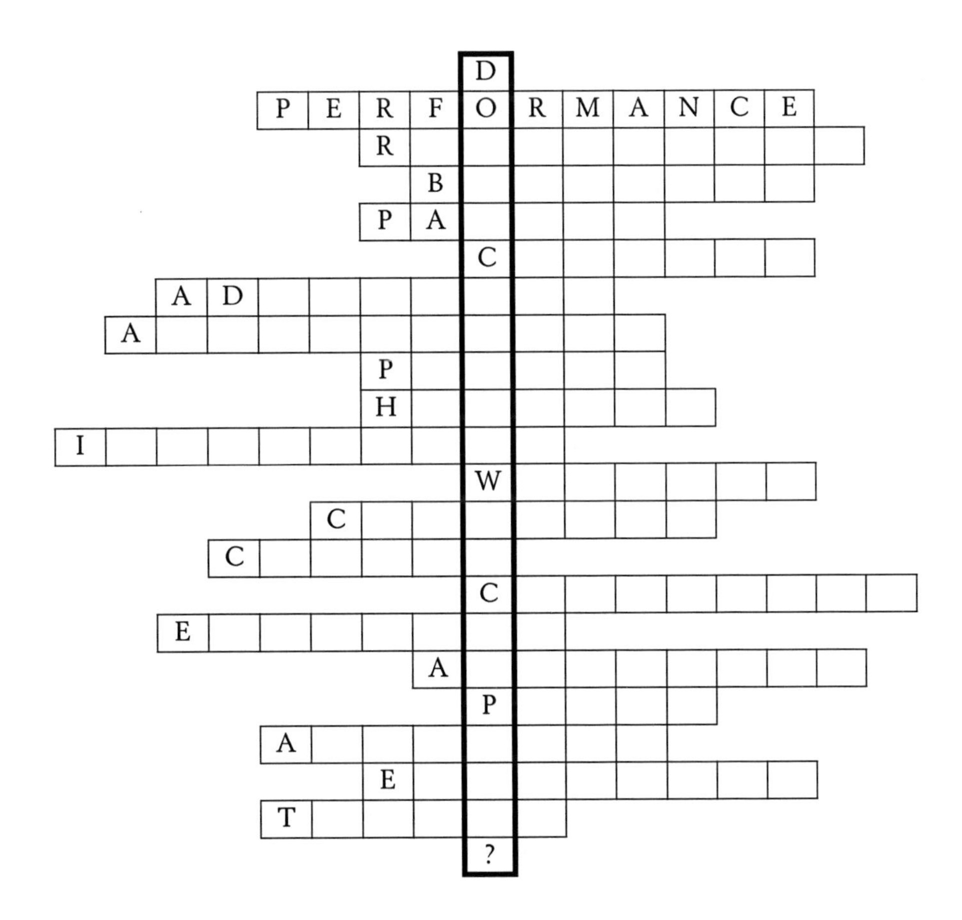

BONUS! The puzzle has a secret silly sentence. It reads from the top of the puzzle down. Write the puzzle's secret silly sentence here:

____

EXERCISE 6
DAFFY DEFINITIONS

Name ________________________________

Date ________________________________

Choose the correct definition for each word. Circle the letter in front of the definition you choose.

1. party
   (a) one part of a thing
   (b) tiny animal
   (c) fun group event

2. birthday
   (a) day of birth
   (b) day of death
   (c) first day of each month

3. adventure
   (a) dull, boring time
   (b) exciting event
   (c) false teeth

4. picnic
   (a) informal outdoor meal
   (b) picky person
   (c) annoying itch

5. holiday
   (a) holy day
   (b) extra-long work day
   (c) day off from work or school

6. travel
   (a) cloth for drying
   (b) garden tool
   (c) go on a trip

7. wedding
   (a) funeral
   (b) marriage ceremony
   (c) metal-working skill

8. parade
   (a) street procession
   (b) TV movie
   (c) long speech

9. contest
   (a) end-of-term exam
   (b) game or race you try to win
   (c) tight-fitting garment

10. celebrate
   (a) break the rules
   (b) honor a special day
   (c) stay away from people

EXERCISE 6 *(continued)*

DAFFY DEFINITIONS

Name ______________________________

Date ______________________________

(BONUS! Continue to choose the correct definition for each word.)

11. circus
    - (a) petting zoo
    - (b) show with trained animals and clowns
    - (c) perfect circle

12. election
    - (a) course of study
    - (b) form of home energy
    - (c) voting event

13. invitation
    - (a) request to attend
    - (b) refusal to attend
    - (c) expensive gift

14. entertain
    - (a) interest and amuse
    - (b) put to sleep
    - (c) ride on a train

15. audience
    - (a) dance party
    - (b) group that watches
    - (c) healing herb

16. carnival
    - (a) red flower
    - (b) meat-eating animal
    - (c) fair with rides and games

17. performance
    - (a) program that entertains
    - (b) type of rectangle
    - (c) high platform

18. amusement
    - (a) long silence
    - (b) mouse hunt
    - (c) thing that makes you happy and pleased

19. anniversary
    - (a) sworn enemy
    - (b) special annual date
    - (c) long written letter

20. recreation
    - (a) hobby or sport
    - (b) thin pancake
    - (c) wrecking crew

EXERCISE 7

SENTENCE SENSE

Name ______________________________

Date ______________________________

Choose an ending that makes sense for each sentence. Circle the letter in front of the ending you choose. The vocabulary word (or words) in each sentence is underlined.

1. At her <u>party</u>, Kristy had
   (a) music and dancing.
   (b) long lectures and tests.
   (c) hard and boring jobs to do.
2. A <u>holiday</u> means I don't have to
   (a) brush my teeth.
   (b) eat any food.
   (c) go to work.
3. Our <u>adventure</u> was
   (a) a boring book.
   (b) exciting and fun.
   (c) a greedy relative.
4. On their <u>picnic</u>, the family brought along
   (a) all their camels and lions.
   (b) lots of food and drink.
   (c) their house and carpet.
5. My favorite way to <u>travel</u> is
   (a) by bus.
   (b) by swallowing.
   (c) upside down.
6. On her fifth <u>birthday</u>, Vanessa was
   (a) ten years old.
   (b) born.
   (c) five years old.
7. The most important people at a <u>wedding</u> are the
   (a) teacher and students.
   (b) bride and groom.
   (c) boss and employees.
8. Most often, a <u>parade</u> takes place
   (a) at a bank.
   (b) inside a house.
   (c) on a public street.
9. Ali won the <u>contest</u> by
   (a) doing better than the others.
   (b) quitting before starting.
   (c) losing.
10. Mike chose to <u>celebrate</u> the special event by
    (a) ignoring it.
    (b) having a party.
    (c) sneezing at it.

EXERCISE 7 *(continued)*

Name ______________________________

SENTENCE SENSE

Date ______________________________

(BONUS! Continue to choose the correct ending for each sentence.)

11. At a circus, you will most likely see
    (a) football players.
    (b) ant farms and rock samples.
    (c) elephants and clowns.
12. Kim ran for election as
    (a) union president.
    (b) a track star.
    (c) a great escape.
13. The invitation said
    (a) "Stay away!"
    (b) "Please attend."
    (c) "You are under arrest."
14. To entertain the guests, Omar
    (a) got angry and yelled.
    (b) went to sleep.
    (c) told a ghost story.
15. The drama club wanted a large audience
    (a) for their stage play.
    (b) to clean the building.
    (c) to sell tickets outside.
16. At the carnival, you can
    (a) build a skyscraper.
    (b) win prizes by playing games.
    (c) adopt a baby.
17. We enjoyed the performance put on by the
    (a) marching band.
    (b) picture window.
    (c) bicycle path.
18. To amuse myself, I like to
    (a) do a chore I don't want to do.
    (b) get sick.
    (c) watch a funny movie.
19. Today is the anniversary of
    (a) last night's supper.
    (b) the merry-go-round.
    (c) the day we met.
20. In a public recreation area, people
    (a) work and complain.
    (b) relax and play.
    (c) have to stay away.

EXERCISE 8
CROSSWORD CHALLENGE

Name ______________________

Date ______________________

Use the numbered clues to fill in the crossword grid. Some of the letters have been filled in already.

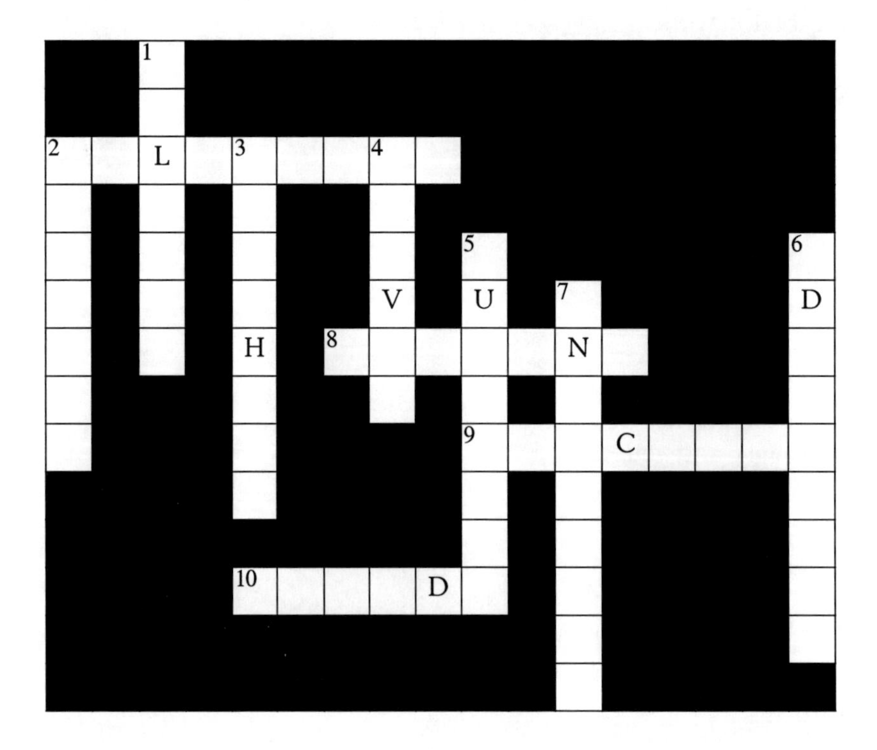

Across

2. Honor a special day
8. Marriage ceremony
9. Choosing by voting
10. Public march

Down

1. Day off from work
2. Game you try to win
3. Day you were born
4. Make a trip
5. Group of people who watch
6. Exciting experience
7. Amuse and interest someone

Unit 5

CHILD CARE WORDS

EXERCISE 1
WORD SENSE

Name ______________________________

Date ______________________________

Read each word below and its definition. Rewrite each word in the blanks next to its definition.

	Word	Definition	Blanks
1.	pacifier	nipple-shaped device that babies suck on	_ _ [c] _ _ _ _ _
2.	teething	first growth of teeth in a baby or young child	_ _ _ _ [h] _ _ _
3.	immunization	shot or liquid drops that protect a baby or young child from certain illnesses; also called inoculation	_ _ _ _ _ _ _ [a] _ _ _ _
4.	infant	child during the earliest period of life; baby	_ [n] _ _ _ _
5.	high chair	child's chair with long legs, a footrest, and a feeding tray	_ _ [g] _ _ _ _ _ _
6.	toddler	young child, about one to three years old, who walks in short, tottering steps	_ _ _ _ _ [e] _
7.	stroller	chair on wheels in which a baby sits and is pushed along	_ [t] _ _ _ _ _ _
8.	preschool	activity and play school for children about three to four years old	_ _ _ _ _ [h] _ _ _
9.	nursery	baby's bedroom; a place where young children are cared for	_ _ _ _ [e] _ _
10.	bottle	container to hold liquids, from which a baby drinks	[b] _ _ _ _ _
11.	nap	short sleep; or, to sleep for a short time	_ [a] _
12.	crib	small bed with high sides for a baby	_ _ _ [b]
13.	day care	group care for children whose parents work away from home	_ _ [y] _ _ _ _
14.	nurse	to feed milk to a baby through a nipple; or, person who takes care of children or sick people	_ _ _ [s] _
15.	diaper	underwear for a baby made or lined with soft material	[d] _ _ _ _ _
16.	bib	piece of cloth or plastic tied under a child's chin to protect the clothes	_ [i] _
17.	playpen	small pen that folds up easily; a baby can play in it	_ _ [a] _ _ _ _
18.	nipple	rubber tip of a baby's bottle, or small rounded tip of a breast; a baby sucks on it to get milk	_ _ _ [p] _ _
19.	baby-sitter	person who takes care of a child while the parents are away for a while	_ _ _ _ - _ _ _ _ [e] _
20.	formula	milk (or other liquid) mixture fed to a baby instead of breast milk	_ _ [r] _ _ _ _

BONUS! The boxed letters spell out a sentence. What does it say? (Write it out here if you want to:) ______________________________

EXERCISE 2
FUN FILL-INS

Name ______________________________

Date ______________________________

Each sentence below has a word (or two words together) missing. Fill in each blank with a word that makes sense from the list at the top of this page. Check off each word in the list as you use it.

nap	stroller	baby-sitter
bib	bottle	playpen
crib	diaper	toddler
	nurse	

1. Always use a _ _ b when you feed the baby.
2. Something smells! You'd better change the baby's _ i _ p _ _ .
3. Teresa put her baby in the p _ _ y _ _ _ when she went to answer the doorbell.
4. I push my young child to the playground in her _ _ r _ _ l _ _ .
5. My two-year-old knows how to climb out of her _ r _ _ by herself.
6. A nurse at the hospital showed Cherise how to _ u _ _ _ her baby.
7. A _ _ b _ - _ _ t _ e _ stayed with our child when we went out.
8. Marco's baby drank everything in his _ _ t _ _ _.
9. When Anna began to walk, she became a t _ _ d _ _ _ .
10. Will put his fussy baby down for a _ a _.

EXERCISE 2 *(continued)*

FUN FILL-INS

Name ______________________________

Date ______________________________

(BONUS! Continue to fill in the blanks from the word list at the top of this page.)

infant	pacifier	day care
nipple	nursery	preschool
teething	formula	immunization
	high chair	

11. We turned our small spare room into the baby's _ u _ _ _ _ y.

12. Don't ever leave your young child alone in the _ _ g _   _ h _ _ _.

13. A two-week-old i _ _ _ n _ is very small.

14. Bianca feeds her baby _ _ r _ u _ _ instead of breast milk.

15. My child plays games and eats snacks at his p _ _ _ c _ _ o _.

16. Rub an ice cube on baby's gums to soothe _ e _ _ h _ _ _ pain.

17. Ian's baby loves to suck on his _ _ c _ f _ _ _.

18. This _ m _ _ _ i _ _ t _ _ _ will protect your child against polio.

19. While Denzel is at work, his child is at _ _ y   _ _ r _.

20. A baby gets milk when she sucks on the n _ _ p _ _.

Exercise 3
Hidden Words

Name ______________________

Date ______________________

Read the following story. Draw a line under each word from the list below when you first find the word in the story. Check off each word in the list as you find it. The first one is done as an example.

bib	diaper	teething	baby-sitter	immunizations
crib	nurse	stroller	preschool	✔ day care
nap	toddler	infant	formula	nursery
bottle	playpen	nipple	pacifier	high chair

Some parents take their baby to day care. Others send their young child to preschool. At home, parents hire a baby-sitter. Here are some tips on being a good baby-sitter. You must know how to take care of an infant and a toddler. You nurse a baby with a bottle. Fill the bottle with formula. Then put on a clean nipple. A toddler can eat in a high chair, wearing a bib. When a baby is tired, bring her to her nursery. Put her down for a nap in her crib. Later, she might enjoy her toys in the playpen. Change the diaper when it's wet. Give a teething baby a cold pacifier to suck on. Or take a fussy child for a walk in the stroller. It's the parents' job to be sure a young child gets all of his immunizations.

Now write each word you marked in the story on the lines below.

day care	________	________
________	________	________
________	________	________
________	________	________
________	________	________
________	________	________
________	________	

EXERCISE 4

LUCKY LISTS

Name ______________________________

Date ______________________________

Each word in the list at the top of this page belongs in one of the categories listed below. Write each word under the category it belongs to. The first word in two columns is done as an example. Check off each word in the list as you use it.

✔ bib	diaper	teething	baby-sitter	immunization
✔ crib	nurse	stroller	nursery	day care
nap	toddler	infant	formula	preschool
bottle	playpen	nipple	pacifier	high chair

Things relating to feeding

bib
____
____
____
____

Baby equipment and baby room

crib
____
____
____
____
____
____

Types of child care

____
____
____

Types of young children

____
____

Things that make baby unhappy

____
____

Thing baby needs to do a lot

____

EXERCISE 5
PUZZLE TIME

Name ______________________

Date ______________________

Fill in the boxes in the puzzle with words that fit from the word list at the top of this page. Check the words off in the list as you use them. The first letter (and sometimes another letter) of each word is given. The first word is done as an example.

bib	diaper	teething	✔ baby-sitter	immunization
crib	nurse	stroller	nursery	day care
nap	toddler	infant	formula	preschool
bottle	playpen	nipple	pacifier	high chair

BONUS! The puzzle has a secret silly sentence. It reads from the top of the puzzle down. Write the puzzle's secret silly sentence here:

____

EXERCISE 6
DAFFY DEFINITIONS

Name ______________________

Date ______________________

Choose the correct definition for each word. Circle the letter in front of the definition you choose.

1. bottle
   (a) slop bucket
   (b) container for baby's liquids
   (c) plate for baby's food

2. crib
   (a) baby's bed
   (b) childhood disease
   (c) seashore animal

3. nap
   (a) long, deep sleep
   (b) tiny bite
   (c) short sleep

4. bib
   (a) boy's name
   (b) sassy child
   (c) cloth that protects

5. nurse
   (a) pout and mope
   (b) feed from a nipple
   (c) make someone sick

6. diaper
   (a) baby's underwear
   (b) baby's head covering
   (c) baby's bathtub

7. playpen
   (a) corral for horses
   (b) public playground
   (c) folding pen

8. stroller
   (a) table on wheels
   (b) chair on wheels
   (c) long-distance runner

9. toddler
   (a) child who crawls but doesn't walk
   (b) child who's beginning to walk
   (c) teller of tales

10. baby-sitter
    (a) non-parent who takes care of a child
    (b) person who takes a child away
    (c) person who likes to sit on babies

EXERCISE 6 *(continued)*

DAFFY DEFINITIONS

Name ________________________________

Date ________________________________

(BONUS! Continue to choose the correct definition for each word.)

11. infant
    (a) toddler
    (b) teenager
    (c) newly born baby

12. nipple
    (a) rounded tip
    (b) sip of soda
    (c) small serving of food

13. formula
    (a) stiff formal clothes
    (b) baby's milk mixture
    (c) odd shape

14. nursery
    (a) group of nurses
    (b) herd of kittens
    (c) baby's room

15. teething
    (a) three joined rings
    (b) first growth of teeth
    (c) grove of trees

16. pacifier
    (a) nipple-shaped object to suck on
    (b) sleeping powder
    (c) Pacific Ocean boat

17. day care
    (a) group child care
    (b) list of daily tasks
    (c) doctor's orders

18. immunization
    (a) get out of jail free token
    (b) long holiday trip
    (c) shot that protects against illness

19. high chair
    (a) child's rocking chair
    (b) child's chair with long legs
    (c) act of charity

20. preschool
    (a) high school
    (b) no school at all
    (c) activity center for young children

EXERCISE 7
SENTENCE SENSE

Name ______________________

Date ______________________

Choose an ending that makes sense for each sentence. Circle the letter in front of the ending you choose. The vocabulary word (or words) in each sentence is underlined.

1. I filled the baby's bottle with
   (a) carrots and mashed potatoes.
   (b) soda.
   (c) a milk mixture.
2. The baby usually takes a nap
   (a) for two hours.
   (b) all night.
   (c) while she's eating.
3. Tina nurses her baby with breast milk. So she does not use a
   (a) nipple.
   (b) diaper.
   (c) bottle.
4. At meal time, little Bryan's bib
   (a) eats some of the food.
   (b) gets coated with food.
   (c) feeds him.
5. When the baby-sitter arrived, the parents
   (a) went out for the evening.
   (b) stayed home.
   (c) took the children away.
6. Diego changes his baby's diaper
   (a) when it is wet.
   (b) when it is dry.
   (c) up in a tree.
7. Robyn puts her baby in the crib
   (a) when it's play time.
   (b) to give the baby a bath.
   (c) when it's nap time.
8. In the playpen, baby Jen
   (a) plays on the swing set.
   (b) rolls around.
   (c) reads a book.
9. Use the stroller to
   (a) change the baby.
   (b) take the child for a walk.
   (c) change the TV channel.
10. When a toddler walks, she
   (a) is steady and sure.
   (b) sits down at all times.
   (c) is a bit unsteady on her feet.

EXERCISE 7 *(continued)*

SENTENCE SENSE

Name ______________________________

Date ______________________________

(BONUS! Continue to choose the correct ending for each sentence.)

11. A pacifier helps to
    (a) calm and soothe a baby.
    (b) get a baby excited.
    (c) pay for a baby-sitter.
12. At a day care center, children
    (a) sleep all day.
    (b) work all day.
    (c) play and learn.
13. An immunization protects a child from
    (a) monsters.
    (b) an illness.
    (c) child abuse.
14. The hospital nursery was full of
    (a) bicycles.
    (b) goats.
    (c) infants.
15. Andy put the clean nipple on the
    (a) baby's bottle.
    (b) gas tank.
    (c) flagpole.
16. My preschool child is
    (a) seven years old.
    (b) three years old.
    (c) fifteen years old.
17. Teething makes a baby
    (a) very happy.
    (b) a good student.
    (c) fussy.
18. My baby's formula is made mostly of
    (a) apple pie.
    (b) fizzy soda.
    (c) cow's milk.
19. I put my child in a high chair
    (a) at meal times.
    (b) to learn to swim.
    (c) under the table.
20. An infant mostly
    (a) reads and writes.
    (b) eats and sleeps.
    (c) gives speeches.

EXERCISE 8
CROSSWORD CHALLENGE

Name ______________________

Date ______________________

Use the numbered clues to fill in the crossword grid. Some of the letters have been filled in already.

Across

1. First growth of teeth
5. Feed milk to baby
7. Baby's wheeled chair
9. Container baby drinks from
10. Nipple-shaped device to suck on
11. Short sleep

Down

2. Young child learning to walk
3. Very young baby
4. Milk mixture for baby to drink
6. Baby's bed
8. Baby's safe place to play

Unit 6

Tool and Machine Words

EXERCISE 1
WORD SENSE

Name ______________________________

Date ______________________________

Read each word below and its definition. Rewrite each word in the blanks next to its definition.

No.	Word	Definition	Answer
1.	pump	machine used to move liquids or gas from one place to another	_ [u] _ _
2.	saw	tool that has a sharp metal blade with teeth on one edge, used for cutting	[s] _ _
3.	wrench	tool with jaws, used to grip and turn a nut or bolt	_ _ [e] _ _ _
4.	staple	bent piece of metal used to hold things together; also, to attach with staples	_ _ [a] _ _ _
5.	ladder	structure used for climbing, made of step pieces attached to two long pieces	_ _ _ [d] _ _
6.	furnace	enclosed structure in which heat is produced	_ _ [r] _ _ _ _
7.	incinerator	furnace that burns garbage or trash	_ _ _ [i] _ _ _ _ _ _ _
8.	lawn mower	machine with blades for cutting grass	[l] _ _ _ _ _ _ _ _
9.	drill	tool used to cut holes in hard materials, like wood and plastic	_ _ _ _ [l]
10.	tool	hand-held device used in doing work	[t] _ _ _
11.	scissors	hand tool with two blades used for cutting	_ _ _ _ _ [o] _ _
12.	hammer	tool with a heavy metal head on a long handle, used to drive nails	_ _ [m] _ _ _
13.	machine	device that does some particular job; made of moving or fixed parts that work together	_ [a] _ _ _ _ _
14.	sprinkler	device that scatters a liquid in fine drops, used to water lawns and gardens or put out fires	_ _ _ _ _ [k] _ _ _
15.	needle	thin, pointed tool with a hole in one end, used in sewing	_ _ [e] _ _ _
16.	shovel	tool with a broad scoop, used for digging and moving loose material	_ [h] _ _ _ _
17.	lock	fastener for a door, window, etc.; you need a special key to open it	_ [o] _ _
18.	appliance	small machine with a particular use, usually found in the home	_ _ _ [l] _ _ _ _ _
19.	pliers	tool made for gripping or bending things, and sometimes for cutting wire	_ _ _ [e] _ _
20.	screwdriver	tool for turning a screw (a nail with ridges, and a slot on its head)	[s] _ _ _ _ _ _ _ _ _ _

BONUS! The boxed letters spell out a sentence. What does it say? (Write it out here if you want to:)

____

EXERCISE 2
FUN FILL-INS

Name ______________________________

Date ______________________________

Each sentence below has a word (or two words together) missing. Fill in each blank with a word that makes sense from the list at the top of this page. Check off each word in the list as you use it.

tools	hammer	pump
saw	ladder	shovel
lock	needle	machines
	scissors	

1. I climbed a _ _ d _ _ _ to get to the roof.
2. A factory is full of many m _ _ _ _ n _ _.
3. Use the _ c _ _ s _ _ _ to cut the paper in half.
4. Tara cut the piece of wood with her _ _ w.
5. Hussein used his _ _ m _ _ _ to drive the nails into the wall.
6. My dog and I dug holes in the back yard. Fido used his paws. I used a _ _ _ v _ _.
7. You can repair rips in your clothes with a _ _ e _ l _ and thread.
8. Always _ _ _ k the door when you leave home.
9. You can fix lots of things in your home with a few simple _ _ o _ _.
10. We used a _ u _ _ to get the water out of the cellar.

EXERCISE 2 *(continued)*

FUN FILL-INS

Name ______________________

Date ______________________

(BONUS! Continue to fill in the blanks from the word list at the top of this page.)

drill	screwdriver	wrench
staple	incinerator	furnace
pliers	lawn mower	sprinkler
	appliance	

11. If a fire starts, the _ p _ _ _ k _ _ _ will come on.

12. We burn our trash in our building's i _ _ _ n _ _ _ t _ _.

13. Grip the wire with the _ l _ _ _ _.

14. Clare used her s _ _ _ w _ _ _ v _ _ to tighten the screw.

15. The _ u _ _ _ c _ keeps our whole building warm.

16. A toaster is a handy kitchen _ _ p _ _ a _ _ _.

17. It's easy to make holes when you use a power _ _ _ l _.

18. When the grass gets long, I bring out the _ _ w _   m _ _ _ _.

19. Use a w _ _ _ _ _ to turn a nut or bolt.

20. When I turn in my report, I'll s _ _ _ l _ the pages together.

EXERCISE 3

HIDDEN WORDS

Name ____________________

Date ____________________

Read the following story. Draw a line under each word from the list below when you first find the word in the story. Check off each word in the list as you find it. The first one is done as an example.

pump	hammer	shovel	wrench	screwdriver
✔tools	ladder	drill	furnace	lawn mower
saw	scissors	staple	sprinkler	incinerator
lock	needle	pliers	machine	appliance

My job is to take care of this apartment building. I have many hand <u>tools</u> to do repairs. My wrench and pliers help with nuts and bolts. I can secure loose things with my hammer or my staple gun. I use my screwdriver to put in a new lock. My power drill also drives and takes out screws. My needle and scissors come in handy, too. I use them to fix the ripped curtains in the entrance. I also make sure each machine and appliance is working well. I use my ladder to check out the sprinkler system. I clean the furnace often. I also make sure the pump and the incinerator are always in running order. Outdoors, I use my saw to cut up any broken tree branches. I cut the grass with the lawn mower in the summer. In the winter, I shovel snow. My job keeps me very busy!

Now write each word you marked in the story on the lines below.

tools	____________	____________
____________	____________	____________
____________	____________	____________
____________	____________	____________
____________	____________	____________
____________	____________	____________
____________	____________	

Exercise 4

Lucky Lists

Name ______________________

Date ______________________

Each word in the list at the top of this page belongs in one of the categories listed below. Write each word under the category it belongs to. The first word in two columns is done as an example. Check off each word in the list as you use it.

✔pump	✔hammer	shovel	wrench	screwdriver
tool	ladder	drill	furnace	lawn mower
saw	scissors	staple	sprinkler	incinerator
lock	needle	pliers	machine	appliance

Machines

pump
____
____
____
____
____

Gripping, turning, fastening, and driving tools

hammer
____
____
____
____
____
____

Cutting and digging tools

____
____
____

Something you'd find on a door

____

Words for the words in this unit

____
____

Something you use to climb

____

EXERCISE 5

PUZZLE TIME

Name ______________________________

Date ______________________________

Fill in the boxes in the puzzle with words that fit from the word list at the top of this page. Check the words off in the list as you use them. The first letter (and sometimes another letter) of each word is given. The first word is done as an example.

pump	hammer	shovel	wrench	screwdriver
tool	ladder	drill	furnace	lawn mower
✔saw	scissors	staple	sprinkler	incinerator
lock	needle	pliers	machine	appliance

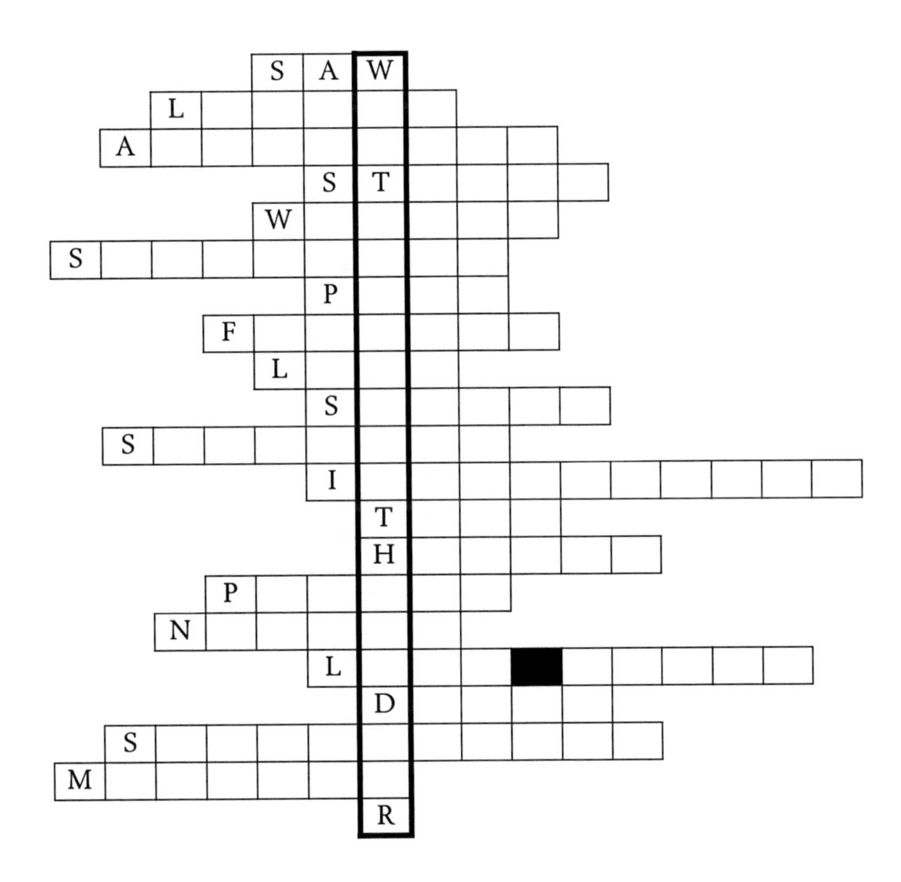

BONUS! The puzzle has a secret silly sentence. It reads from the top of the puzzle down. Write the puzzle's secret silly sentence here:

____

Exercise 6
Daffy Definitions

Name ________________________________

Date ________________________________

Choose the correct definition for each word. Circle the letter in front of the definition you choose.

1. tool
   - (a) work device, like a hammer or saw
   - (b) foolish person or thing
   - (c) useless thing
2. saw
   - (a) tool for drilling holes
   - (b) sound a crow makes
   - (c) cutting tool
3. lock
   - (a) something you do with your tongue
   - (b) door fastener
   - (c) time-keeping device
4. hammer
   - (a) tool for turning a bolt
   - (b) tool for driving nails
   - (c) all-terrain vehicle
5. ladder
   - (a) climbing device
   - (b) part of the alphabet
   - (c) tool for chopping
6. needle
   - (a) trimming tool
   - (b) something you need
   - (c) thin, pointed sewing tool
7. scissors
   - (a) your sharp pointed teeth
   - (b) cutting tool
   - (c) tool that helps you see
8. pump
   - (a) water-moving machine
   - (b) young dog
   - (c) snow removal machine
9. shovel
   - (a) climbing device
   - (b) person who shoves
   - (c) digging tool
10. machine
    - (a) type of soldier
    - (b) device made of moving parts that does a job
    - (c) sharp-ended tack

EXERCISE 6 *(continued)*
DAFFY DEFINITIONS

Name ______________________

Date ______________________

(BONUS! Continue to choose the correct definition for each word.)

11. drill
    (a) deep well
    (b) tool for cutting holes
    (c) tool for chopping

12. staple
    (a) metal fastener
    (b) knotted rope
    (c) place to keep horses

13. pliers
    (a) cutting tool
    (b) untruthful persons
    (c) gripping tool

14. screwdriver
    (a) tool for driving nails
    (b) sheep herder
    (c) tool for turning screws

15. incinerator
    (a) deadly killer
    (b) trash-burning furnace
    (c) air-cooling machine

16. lawn mower
    (a) grass-cutting machine
    (b) garden digging machine
    (c) football field turf

17. appliance
    (a) person you can rely on
    (b) building-sized machine
    (c) small, handy machine

18. wrench
    (a) pointed tool used to sew
    (b) jawed tool used to grip and turn
    (c) small songbird

19. furnace
    (a) machine that receives and sends messages
    (b) heat-producing machine
    (c) fur piece you wear around your neck

20. sprinkler
    (a) watering device
    (b) small pieces of colored candy
    (c) listening device

EXERCISE 7

SENTENCE SENSE

Name ______________________________

Date ______________________________

Choose an ending that makes sense for each sentence. Circle the letter in front of the ending you choose. The vocabulary word (or words) in each sentence is underlined.

1. Scissors are the best tool to use to
   (a) make Swiss cheese.
   (b) cut cloth.
   (c) cut wood.
2. A shovel is an important tool for a
   (a) ditch digger.
   (b) dinner chef.
   (c) mole.
3. I used the ladder to
   (a) climb the mountain.
   (b) dance a jig.
   (c) reach the ceiling.
4. Thanks to the pump,
   (a) the ocean is full of water.
   (b) the swimming pool is full of water.
   (c) we had no water.
5. Cheryl used an electric saw to
   (a) drill holes in the floor.
   (b) see through the walls.
   (c) cut shelves for her bookcase.
6. Using a needle and thread, Jack
   (a) sewed the button back onto his shirt.
   (b) cut the pizza.
   (c) watered the garden.
7. Lock the door so the
   (a) dog stays in.
   (b) burglar can come in.
   (c) TV turns on.
8. In the hammer contest, each person quickly
   (a) hummed two tunes.
   (b) unscrewed screws.
   (c) pounded nails.
9. My set of hand tools includes
   (a) book, pen, and paper.
   (b) hammer, wrench, and pliers.
   (c) fish, pigs, and hens.
10. One type of machine is a(n)
    (a) ladder.
    (b) grandfather.
    (c) engine.

EXERCISE 7 *(continued)*

Name ______________________________

SENTENCE SENSE

Date ______________________________

(BONUS! Continue to choose the correct ending for each sentence.)

11. When I was done, the <u>staples</u>
    (a) lit up the room.
    (b) held the screen on the door.
    (c) said thank-you.
12. The <u>appliance</u> repair shop
    (a) fixed our bicycle.
    (b) sold us a sofa.
    (c) fixed our blender.
13. When the <u>incinerator</u> runs,
    (a) smoke comes out the chimney.
    (b) we run after it.
    (c) the rooms get cold.
14. I needed a <u>wrench</u>
    (a) to cut a square hole.
    (b) to loosen the nut and bolt.
    (c) to get good and wet.
15. We run our <u>lawn mower</u> often
    (a) during the snowy winter.
    (b) to trim Grandpa Fred's hair.
    (c) when the grass is growing.
16. Raquel used her <u>drill</u> to
    (a) record a song.
    (b) start holes for the screws.
    (c) get the core out of the apple.
17. The <u>sprinkler</u> system keeps
    (a) the garden watered.
    (b) things scattered around.
    (c) the cats fed.
18. I used my <u>screwdriver</u> to
    (a) take apart the toy.
    (b) nail the stairs in place.
    (c) drive the scooter to town.
19. While working with the <u>pliers</u>, Tranh
    (a) plugged them into the electric outlet.
    (b) sat on them.
    (c) held them in his hand.
20. Our <u>furnace</u> is
    (a) in the bathtub.
    (b) in the cellar.
    (c) hanging up in the closet.

EXERCISE 8
CROSSWORD CHALLENGE

Name ______________________________

Date ______________________________

Use the numbered clues to fill in the crossword grid. Some of the letters have been filled in already.

Across

5. Tool for turning a screw
8. Door fastener
9. Sewing tool
10. Device that scatters liquid droplets

Down

1. Tool for driving nails
2. Cutting tool
3. Home heat producer
4. Tool for turning nuts and bolts
5. Digging tool
6. Structure for climbing
7. Tool for gripping

Unit 7

Cooking Words

EXERCISE 1
WORD SENSE

Name ______________________________

Date ______________________________

Read each word below and its definition. Rewrite each word in the blanks next to its definition.

1.	recipe	list of instructions for making something to eat or drink	_ _ _ [i] _ _
2.	saucepan	small, deep cooking pan with a handle	_ _ _ [c] _ _ _ _
3.	fork	eating tool with thin, pointed parts at the end of a handle	_ [o] _ _
4.	oven	enclosed space used to heat, bake, or roast food placed inside it	[o] _ _ _
5.	skillet	shallow cooking pan with a handle; frying pan	_ [k] _ _ _ _ _
6.	blender	small kitchen machine that grinds and mixes food together	_ _ _ _ [d] _ _
7.	dishwasher	machine that washes dishes, glasses, utensils, and pots	_ [i] _ _ _ _ _ _ _ _
8.	utensils	objects or tools useful for cooking	_ _ _ [n] _ _ _ _
9.	ingredients	parts that go into a mixture or a recipe	_ [n] _ _ _ _ _ _ _ _ _
10.	toaster	small kitchen machine that browns slices of bread	_ _ _ _ _ [e] _
11.	casserole	deep dish in which you can cook and serve food; also, the food cooked in a casserole	_ _ _ _ _ [r] _ _ _
12.	dinner	the main meal of the day	_ [i] _ _ _ _
13.	hungry	wanting or needing food	_ _ [n] _ _ _
14.	nutrition	food; nourishment	_ _ _ _ _ [t] _ _ _
15.	thirsty	feeling a need to drink something	_ [h] _ _ _ _ _
16.	knife	cutting tool with a sharp blade at the end of a handle	_ _ _ _ [e]
17.	cookbook	book of cooking instructions and recipes	_ _ _ _ _ _ [o] _
18.	silverware	spoons, forks, or knives made of metal	_ _ _ [v] _ _ _ _ _ _
19.	measure	to find or show the size, weight, or amount of something	_ [e] _ _ _ _ _
20.	spoon	eating utensil with a small, shallow bowl at the end of a handle	_ _ _ _ [n]

BONUS! The boxed letters spell out a sentence. What does it say? (Write it out here if you want to:)

____

EXERCISE 2
FUN FILL-INS

Name ______________________________

Date ______________________________

Each sentence below has a word missing. Fill in each blank with a word that makes sense from the list at the top of this page. Check off each word in the list as you use it.

dinner	spoon	measure
hungry	oven	blender
thirsty	fork	cookbook
	knife	

1. I was so _ u _ g _ _, I ate every bit of food on my plate.
2. Stir the soup with a _ _ _ _ n while it heats up.
3. Alex made a milkshake in the b _ _ _ d _ _.
4. Use the _ _ _ f _ to cut your steak.
5. We always eat _ i _ n _ _ at 6 o'clock.
6. You can eat the meal with a _ _ _ k or with chopsticks.
7. M _ _ _ u _ _ one cup of flour for the pancakes.
8. Drink a glass of cool water when you're _ h _ _ _ _ y.
9. My favorite _ _ o _ b _ _ _ is *The Joy of Cooking.*
10. Bake the cake in the _ v _ _.

EXERCISE 2 *(continued)*

FUN FILL-INS

Name ______________________________

Date ______________________________

(BONUS! Continue to fill in the blanks from the word list at the top of this page.)

toaster	dishwasher	saucepan
utensils	silverware	recipe
casserole	ingredients	skillet
	nutrition	

11. Put the s _ _ v _ _ _ a _ _ on the table next to the plates.

12. LaToya cooked the bacon in her _ k _ _ l _ _.

13. Darn! The _ _ a _ t _ _ burned the bread.

14. Each person brought a _ _ s _ _ r _ _ e to the pot-luck dinner.

15. Most food labels have a list of "N _ _ r _ _ i _ _ Facts."

16. I need a good _ e _ _ p _ for chicken salad.

17. Put the dirty dishes in the d _ _ _ w _ _ h _ _.

18. Pedro boiled an egg in his _ _ u _ _ p _ _.

19. The label on the jar lists all of the salsa's i _ _ r _ _ i _ _ _ _.

20. I keep my kitchen _ t _ _ s _ _ _ next to the stove.

EXERCISE 3
HIDDEN WORDS

Name ____________________

Date ____________________

Read the following story. Draw a line under each word from the list below when you first find the word in the story. Check off each word in the list as you find it. The first one is done as an example.

✔dinner	hungry	cookbook	ingredients	casserole
spoon	thirsty	measure	dishwasher	saucepan
knife	toaster	utensils	silverware	skillet
oven	fork	blender	nutrition	recipe

Today it is my turn to make dinner. I found a new recipe to try in the cookbook. First I measure out all the ingredients. Then I mix them in the blender. Next, I heat the mix in a saucepan and stir with a spoon. Then I pour the mix into a casserole. I bake it in the oven for half an hour. Meanwhile, I cook the meat in a skillet. I also bring the silverware to the table. Next to each plate, I put a knife and a fork. Each thirsty person gets a glass of ice water. Just before I serve the meal, I heat the bread in the toaster. I also put all the used utensils in the dishwasher. Then I call everyone to the table. My meal offers all of us good nutrition. It's tasty, too! I hope we are all hungry!

Now write each word you marked in the story on the lines below.

dinner	____________	____________
____________	____________	____________
____________	____________	____________
____________	____________	____________
____________	____________	____________
____________	____________	____________
____________	____________	

EXERCISE 4
LUCKY LISTS

Name ______________________________

Date ______________________________

Each word in the list at the top of this page belongs in one of the categories listed below. Write each word under the category it belongs to. The first word in two columns is done as an example. Check off each word in the list as you use it.

dinner	hungry	cookbook	ingredients	casserole
✔spoon	thirsty	measure	dishwasher	saucepan
knife	toaster	utensils	silverware	skillet
✔oven	fork	blender	nutrition	recipe

Things you cook food in

oven
____
____
____
____

Things you eat and mix food with

spoon
____
____
____
____
____

Words related to eating and drinking

____
____
____
____

Things related to recipes

____
____
____
____

Things you use to clean cooking items

____

EXERCISE 5
PUZZLE TIME

Name ______________________________

Date ______________________________

Fill in the boxes in the puzzle with words that fit from the word list at the top of this page. Check the words off in the list as you use them. The first letter (and sometimes another letter) of each word is given. The first word is done as an example.

dinner	hungry	cookbook	ingredients	casserole
spoon	thirsty	measure	dishwasher	saucepan
knife	toaster	utensils	silverware	skillet
oven	fork	✔blender	nutrition	recipe

BONUS! The puzzle has a secret silly sentence. It reads from the top of the puzzle down. Write the puzzle's secret silly sentence here:

____

EXERCISE 6
DAFFY DEFINITIONS

Name ______________________________

Date ______________________________

Choose the correct definition for each word. Circle the letter in front of the definition you choose.

1. hungry
   (a) needing a drink
   (b) name of a foreign country
   (c) wanting food

2. knife
   (a) cutting tool
   (b) old-time soldier
   (c) mashing tool

3. oven
   (a) stovetop
   (b) food baker
   (c) not closed

4. dinner
   (a) light snack
   (b) main meal
   (c) place to eat out

5. thirsty
   (a) needing food
   (b) cooking a meal
   (c) wanting a drink

6. spoon
   (a) eating utensil with a small bowl
   (b) grilling device
   (c) fainting spell

7. measure
   (a) spend money
   (b) throw out food
   (c) find an amount of something

8. fork
   (a) cutting tool
   (b) eating utensil with prongs
   (c) tasty noodles

9. cookbook
   (a) source of recipes
   (b) master chef
   (c) book that you cook

10. saucepan
   (a) flat shallow cooking pan
   (b) small deep cooking pot
   (c) tall bottle for liquids

EXERCISE 6 *(continued)*

DAFFY DEFINITIONS

Name ______________________________

Date ______________________________

(BONUS! Continue to choose the correct definition for each word.)

11. toaster
    - (a) cake baker
    - (b) bread-slice browner
    - (c) bacon fryer

12. casserole
    - (a) long, flowing scarf
    - (b) cream pie
    - (c) deep cooking dish

13. recipe
    - (a) cooking instructions
    - (b) hot spice
    - (c) dried grape

14. silverware
    - (a) metal forks and spoons
    - (b) pewter plates
    - (c) silver-coated speech

15. blender
    - (a) brother who cooks
    - (b) baking machine
    - (c) mixing machine

16. nutrition
    - (a) kitchen waste
    - (b) health-building food
    - (c) type of number

17. skillet
    - (a) stew pot
    - (b) skilled cook
    - (c) frying pan

18. dishwasher
    - (a) machine to wash plates and glasses
    - (b) machine to wash clothes
    - (c) car wash

19. utensils
    - (a) writing tools
    - (b) kitchen tools
    - (c) net-and-racket game

20. ingredients
    - (a) greedy eaters
    - (b) ungrateful diners
    - (c) items in a recipe

EXERCISE 7
SENTENCE SENSE

Name ______________________________

Date ______________________________

Choose an ending that makes sense for each sentence. Circle the letter in front of the ending you choose. The vocabulary word (or words) in each sentence is underlined.

1. I used the spoon to
   (a) clean the sink.
   (b) stir my shake.
   (c) light the fire.
2. When I'm thirsty, I
   (a) think out loud.
   (b) turn off the heat.
   (c) drink some water.
3. We ate dinner
   (a) at the kitchen table.
   (b) in the popcorn bowl.
   (c) tomorrow.
4. Into the blender, Wes dropped
   (a) plates and glasses.
   (b) fruits and nuts.
   (c) alphabet blocks.
5. Use the fork to
   (a) eat the soup.
   (b) eat the rice.
   (c) mop the floor.
6. Donella was hungry, so she
   (a) ran away from the food.
   (b) hunted for her boots.
   (c) ate lunch.
7. I used a knife to
   (a) cut up the carrots.
   (b) comb my hair.
   (c) mash the potatoes.
8. For the pudding, measure out
   (a) the pile of dirt.
   (b) one cup of milk.
   (c) one yard of cloth.
9. In the oven, we
   (a) washed the pans.
   (b) took a nap.
   (c) roasted a turkey.
10. The cookbook gave us
    (a) good recipe ideas.
    (b) advice on being a friend.
    (c) a long speech.

EXERCISE 7 *(continued)*
SENTENCE SENSE

Name ______________________________

Date ______________________________

(BONUS! Continue to choose the correct ending for each sentence.)

11. Damon took all the ingredients and
    (a) mixed them together.
    (b) read them a story.
    (c) dressed up in them.
12. The kitchen utensils I use a lot are
    (a) electric wires and gas lines.
    (b) mice and hamsters.
    (c) mixing spoons and egg beaters.
13. The dishwasher is a handy place to
    (a) take a bath.
    (b) put dirty dishes.
    (c) cook a meat loaf.
14. The recipe calls for
    (a) help.
    (b) rice and beans.
    (c) nails and screws.
15. My toaster always
    (a) frosts the cupcakes.
    (b) keeps the kitchen warm and toasty.
    (c) burns my bagel.
16. Good nutrition is likely to bring you
    (a) good health.
    (b) fame and fortune.
    (c) juicy gossip.
17. A saucepan is good for
    (a) baking bread.
    (b) heating soup.
    (c) wearing on your head.
18. Choose a casserole to
    (a) sit in.
    (b) get cash from.
    (c) cook a mix in the oven.
19. A skillet is your choice for
    (a) becoming expert at skiing.
    (b) frying foods.
    (c) making coffee.
20. Chantal took the silverware out of
    (a) the drawer.
    (b) the flour bin.
    (c) the coal mine.

EXERCISE 8
CROSSWORD CHALLENGE

Name ______________________________

Date ______________________________

Use the numbered clues to fill in the crossword grid. Some of the letters have been filled in already.

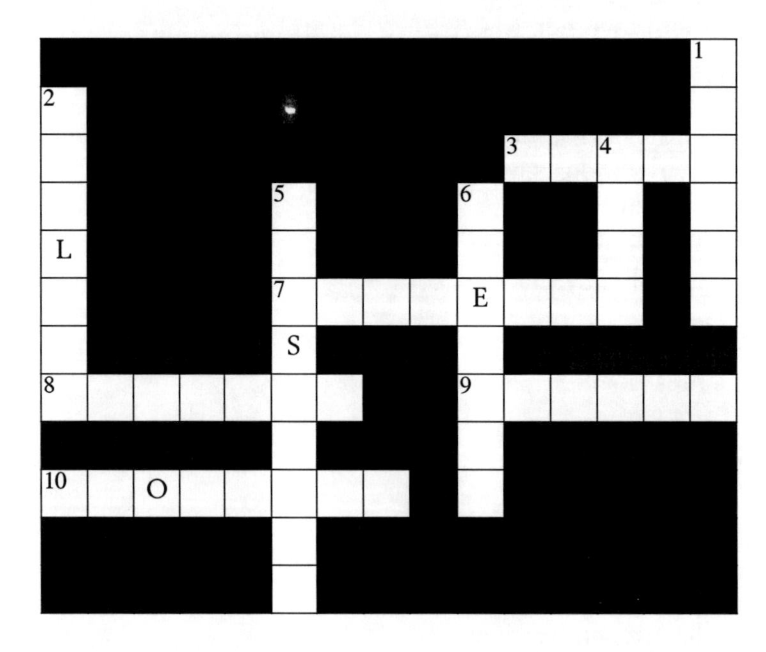

Across

3. Bowl-shaped eating utensil
7. Small, deep cooking pan
8. Small kitchen machine for browning bread
9. Main meal of the day
10. Book of recipes

Down

1. Wanting food
2. Frying pan
4. Food-baking device
5. Deep cooking dish
6. Food-grinding and food-mixing machine

Unit 8

PERSONAL WORDS

EXERCISE 1
WORD SENSE

Name ______________________________

Date ______________________________

Read each word below and its definition. Rewrite each word in the blanks next to its definition.

1.	anxious	nervous, worried, or fearful about what may happen	[a] _ _ _ _ _ _
2.	honest	truthful, fair, and trustworthy	_ _ _ _ [s] _
3.	shy	bashful; not comfortable around other people	_ [h] _
4.	lazy	not willing to work or put out effort	_ _ _ [y]
5.	curious	eager to learn about new, strange, or interesting things	[c] _ _ _ _ _ _
6.	enthusiastic	very excited, eager, and interested about something	_ _ _ [h] _ _ _ _ _ _ _ _
7.	ambitious	having a strong desire to succeed	_ _ _ _ _ [i] _ _ _
8.	jealous	having envy toward a person, or what a person can do	_ _ _ [l] _ _ _
9.	greedy	having a great and selfish desire for more than your share	_ _ _ _ [d] _
10.	impatient	not able to put up with delay or opposition calmly and without anger	_ [m] _ _ _ _ _ _ _
11.	creative	having or showing ability to make new things	_ _ _ [a] _ _ _ _
12.	lonely	unhappy from being alone; away from others	_ _ _ _ _ [y]
13.	stubborn	not willing to give in or yield	_ _ _ _ [b] _ _ _
14.	cheerful	showing or feeling happiness and good spirits	_ _ _ [e] _ _ _ _
15.	selfish	thinking only of yourself, not of others	_ _ [l] _ _ _ _
16.	courageous	brave; willing to face something dangerous, very hard, or painful	_ _ _ _ _ _ _ [o] _ _
17.	vain	too proud of your looks, abilities or accomplishments; conceited	_ _ _ [n]
18.	generous	unselfish; willing and happy to share with others	_ [e] _ _ _ _ _ _
19.	popular	pleasing to very many people; well liked	_ _ _ _ [l] _ _
20.	sympathetic	feeling or showing kindness and pity	_ [y] _ _ _ _ _ _ _ _ _

BONUS! The boxed letters spell out a sentence. What does it say? (Write it out here if you want to:)

____

EXERCISE 2
FUN FILL-INS

Name ______________________________

Date ______________________________

Each sentence below has a word missing. Fill in each blank with a word that makes sense from the list at the top of this page. Check off each word in the list as you use it.

shy	selfish	popular
lazy	curious	cheerful
lonely	honest	stubborn
	greedy	

1. The _ _ z _ dog lies in the sun all day.
2. That _ r _ _ _ y guy wants all the gum.
3. Ice cream is a _ _ p _ _ a _ choice for dessert.
4. The kitten is very _ u _ _ _ _ s about the ball of yarn.
5. My little brother always wants his own way. He is so s _ _ _ b _ _ _!
6. My older sister won't share her clothes with me. I think she's _ _ l _ _ s _!
7. When we moved to a new town, I felt _ _ n _ _ _ at first.
8. It can be hard for a _ h _ person to make new friends.
9. An _ o _ _ s _ person tells no lies.
10. Asha is always so c _ _ _ _ f _ _, she makes me feel happy too.

EXERCISE 2 *(continued)*
FUN FILL-INS

Name ______________________________

Date ______________________________

(BONUS! Continue to fill in the blanks from the word list at the top of this page.)

vain	enthusiastic	jealous
creative	courageous	anxious
ambitious	impatient	generous
	sympathetic	

11. Terrell gets very _ _ p _ t _ _ _ _ if the bus runs late.

12. I feel _ _ x _ _ _ s about what grade I'll get on the exam.

13. We are all very e _ _ _ u _ _ _ s _ _ _ about the picnic we plan to go on.

14. Most of the students in my art class are quite _ r _ _ _ _ v _.

15. Rosa was _ y _ _ _ t _ _ t _ _ toward me when I lost my puppy.

16. I think Rich was c _ _ r _ _ e _ _ _ to stand up to the bully.

17. Please be _ _ n _ r _ _ _. Give money to this good cause.

18. Caryl acts quite _ _ _ n about her good looks.

19. Ahmed plans to be a doctor. He is very a _ _ _ t _ _ _ _.

20. My sister is very popular. Sometimes that makes me feel _ _ _ l _ u _.

EXERCISE 3

HIDDEN WORDS

Name ______________________________

Date ______________________________

Read the following story. Draw a line under each word from the list below when you first find the word in the story. Check off each word in the list as you find it. The first one is done as an example.

shy	selfish	popular	jealous	✔ enthusiastic
lazy	curious	cheerful	anxious	courageous
lonely	honest	stubborn	ambitious	sympathetic
vain	greedy	creative	impatient	generous

People have many kinds of personal traits. If you are <u>enthusiastic</u>, you are eager to do things. If you're curious, you want to learn about new things. If you're creative, you want to make new things. Are you cheerful and honest? Are you sympathetic and generous? If so, you will be popular. If you're ambitious and not lazy, you'll go far. Being courageous will help you face life's troubles. If you think too much of yourself, you are vain. If you're vain, you may also be selfish and greedy. If you're shy, you may feel lonely. If you are jealous, you will feel anxious about your friends. If you insist on doing things your own way, you are stubborn. If you can't stand any kind of delay, you are impatient. Can you tell which of these traits will bring you the most friends?

Now write each word you marked in the story on the lines below.

enthusiastic	____________	____________
____________	____________	____________
____________	____________	____________
____________	____________	____________
____________	____________	____________
____________	____________	____________
____________	____________	

EXERCISE 4
LUCKY LISTS

Name ______________________

Date ______________________

Each word in the list at the top of this page belongs in one of the categories listed below. Write each word under the category it belongs to. The first word in two columns is done as an example. Check off each word in the list as you use it.

shy	selfish	popular	jealous	enthusiastic
lazy	✔curious	cheerful	anxious	courageous
lonely	✔honest	stubborn	ambitious	sympathetic
vain	greedy	creative	impatient	generous

Begins with a letter between *A* and *D*

curious
____
____
____
____
____

Begins with a letter between *E* and *K*

honest
____
____
____
____
____

Begins with a letter between *L* and *R*

____
____
____

Begins with a letter between *S* and *Z*

____
____
____
____
____

EXERCISE 5
PUZZLE TIME

Name ______________________________

Date ______________________________

Fill in the boxes in the puzzle with words that fit from the word list at the top of this page. Check the words off in the list as you use them. The first letter (and sometimes another letter) of each word is given. The first word is done as an example.

shy	selfish	popular	jealous	enthusiastic
lazy	curious	cheerful	anxious	courageous
lonely	honest	stubborn	✔ambitious	sympathetic
vain	greedy	creative	impatient	generous

BONUS! The puzzle has a secret silly sentence. It reads from the top of the puzzle down. Write the puzzle's secret silly sentence here:

____

EXERCISE 6
DAFFY DEFINITIONS

Name ______________________________

Date ______________________________

Choose the correct definition for each word. Circle the letter in front of the definition you choose.

1. cheerful
   (a) feeling gloomy
   (b) acting happy
   (c) clapping and shouting

2. popular
   (a) disliked and avoided
   (b) tall and thin
   (c) liked by many people

3. greedy
   (a) wanting too much
   (b) growling like a bear
   (c) outgoing

4. lonely
   (a) part of a crowd
   (b) away from others
   (c) likely to take action

5. lazy
   (a) unwilling to work
   (b) helpful
   (c) full of energy

6. curious
   (a) very careful
   (b) collector of curios
   (c) eager to learn

7. shy
   (a) grumpy
   (b) bashful
   (c) sleepy

8. stubborn
   (a) flexible
   (b) unwilling to give in
   (c) firstborn

9. honest
   (a) truthful
   (b) angry
   (c) given to lying

10. selfish
   (a) generous
   (b) concerned about others
   (c) unwilling to share

EXERCISE 6 *(continued)*

DAFFY DEFINITIONS

Name ______________________________

Date ______________________________

(BONUS! Continue to choose the correct definition for each word.)

11. impatient
    (a) annoyed by delay
    (b) under a doctor's care
    (c) playful

12. vain
    (a) careless
    (b) humble
    (c) overly proud

13. creative
    (a) fond of animals
    (b) talented at making new things
    (c) likely to destroy things

14. jealous
    (a) trusting and faithful
    (b) having envy toward someone
    (c) wobbly and clumsy

15. anxious
    (a) nervous and worried
    (b) calm and peaceful
    (c) full of daydreams

16. generous
    (a) unwilling to give
    (b) good at taking command
    (c) happy to share

17. ambitious
    (a) talented at swimming
    (b) wanting to succeed
    (c) lazy

18. sympathetic
    (a) kind and sensitive
    (b) deserving of pity
    (c) falsely friendly

19. courageous
    (a) beautiful
    (b) cowardly
    (c) brave

20. enthusiastic
    (a) withdrawn and sullen
    (b) eager and excited
    (c) solemn and serious

EXERCISE 7
SENTENCE SENSE

Name ______________________________

Date ______________________________

Choose an ending that makes sense for each sentence. Circle the letter in front of the ending you choose. The vocabulary word (or words) in each sentence is underlined.

1. Manny was very <u>curious</u> to
   (a) stay at home.
   (b) comb his hair.
   (c) see what was in the locked box.
2. The <u>stubborn</u> little child
   (a) ran along with all the others.
   (b) refused to get in the car.
   (c) helped to pick up the toys.
3. Ted is very <u>popular</u>, so he
   (a) can't get any votes.
   (b) has lots of friends.
   (c) stays away from people.
4. Because I am <u>honest</u>, I
   (a) always tell the truth.
   (b) am clean and well-dressed.
   (c) often tell white lies.
5. My friend Nadine is <u>shy</u>, so she
   (a) only eats cereal.
   (b) is bubbly and outgoing.
   (c) has trouble talking to people she doesn't know well.
6. It's a <u>lonely</u> feeling when you
   (a) play a game with friends.
   (b) are far away from home.
   (c) lend money to a friend.
7. I feel <u>cheerful</u> on a
   (a) bright, sunny day.
   (b) dark, gloomy day.
   (c) bed full of red ants.
8. Because Laura is <u>selfish</u>, she
   (a) helps her neighbor.
   (b) works well with other people.
   (c) thinks only of herself.
9. Rico is too <u>lazy</u> to
   (a) eat or drink.
   (b) lie on the couch.
   (c) walk to his job.
10. The <u>greedy</u> old grump
    (a) took more than his share.
    (b) gave all his things away.
    (c) ate only a tiny bit of the cake.

EXERCISE 7 *(continued)*
SENTENCE SENSE

Name ______________________

Date ______________________

(BONUS! Continue to choose the correct ending for each sentence.)

11. I express my <u>creative</u> side by
    (a) washing the dishes.
    (b) drawing cartoons.
    (c) staring at the ceiling.
12. Ervin is very <u>impatient</u>. If the game doesn't start on time, he
    (a) gets up and leaves.
    (b) smiles and jokes.
    (c) waits calmly.
13. April gets <u>jealous</u> if another student
    (a) fails the test.
    (b) is nice to her.
    (c) gets good grades.
14. It was very <u>generous</u> of you to
    (a) take away my coat.
    (b) give me your extra ticket.
    (c) yell at me.
15. Karl acts quite <u>vain</u> since he
    (a) lost the contest.
    (b) became modest.
    (c) won the award.
16. One type of <u>courageous</u> person is a
    (a) war hero.
    (b) school drop-out.
    (c) fearful deserter.
17. A <u>sympathetic</u> boss
    (a) is kind about workers' problems.
    (b) plays classical music all day.
    (c) is stern and harsh with workers.
18. Erin is <u>anxious</u> about
    (a) relaxing in the hot tub.
    (b) eating the cookie.
    (c) giving the speech.
19. The <u>enthusiastic</u> girl
    (a) refused to play the game.
    (b) jumped into the pool.
    (c) sat and moped.
20. An <u>ambitious</u> person
    (a) finds excuses to avoid work.
    (b) picks fights all the time.
    (c) works hard to get ahead.

EXERCISE 8
CROSSWORD CHALLENGE

Name ______________________________

Date ______________________________

Use the numbered clues to fill in the crossword grid. Some of the letters have been filled in already.

Across

5. Feeling happy and in good spirits
6. Unhappy from being alone
8. Nervous, worried, fearful
9. Good at making new things

Down

1. Willing and happy to share
2. Wanting more than your share
3. Not willing to give in
4. Eager to learn about new things
7. Truthful

Unit 9

COMPUTER WORDS

EXERCISE 1
WORD SENSE

Name ______________________________

Date ______________________________

Read each word below and its definition. Rewrite each word in the blanks next to its definition.

1.	printer	device that prints out information from a computer file	_ _ [i] _ _ _ _
2.	mouse	small handheld device that you roll to move the cursor on the monitor screen	_ _ _ [s] _
3.	browser	software that allows your computer to go to sites on the Internet	_ _ _ _ _ [e] _
4.	on-line	status when a computer is connected to another computer or the Internet	_ [n] - _ _ _ _
5.	disk	thin, flat plate that holds information, inside or outside the computer	[d] _ _ _
6.	modem	device that lets a computer send and receive information via phone lines	_ _ _ [e] _
7.	computer	machine that processes and stores electronic information	_ _ [m] _ _ _ _ _
8.	software	programs or instructions that tell a computer what to do	_ _ _ _ _ [a] _ _
9.	workstation	desktop computer specially set up for office work; area set up for a specific job	_ _ _ _ _ _ _ _ [i] _ _
10.	laptop	small lap-sized portable computer	[l] _ _ _ _ _
11.	monitor	video screen of the computer that shows text and images	_ _ _ _ [t] _ _
12.	cursor	small signal on the screen that shows you where you are in your file	_ _ _ _ [o] _
13.	memory	electronic storage areas in the computer where it holds information	[m] _ _ _ _ _
14.	keyboard	device with keys that you use to enter information into a computer	_ _ [y] _ _ _ _ _
15.	fax	short for *facsimile;* image of a document sent and received over phone lines, often via a computer	[f] _ _
16.	port	small inlet where a cable connects to a computer	_ _ [r] _
17.	e-mail	electronic messages sent and received on a computer	_ - _ _ [i] _
18.	hardware	the parts of a computer system	_ _ _ _ _ _ _ [e]
19.	Internet	worldwide network of computers where you can find and share information	_ [n] _ _ _ _ _ _
20.	drive	part of a computer that reads and writes data to and from disks	[d] _ _ _ _

BONUS! The boxed letters spell out a sentence. What does it say? (Write it out here if you want to:)

____

EXERCISE 2

FUN FILL-INS

Name ______________________________

Date ______________________________

Each sentence below has a word missing. Fill in each blank with a word that makes sense from the list at the top of this page. Check off each word in the list as you use it.

disk	computer	laptop
mouse	memory	e-mail
drive	keyboard	cursor
	printer	

1. A computer _ _ _ s _ fits nicely into your hand.
2. A _ _ y _ _ _ r _ is full of letters and numbers.
3. Lamar used his l _ _ t _ _ while he was riding the subway.
4. The _ _ _ s _ _ shows you where you are on the screen.
5. Save your work on a back-up floppy _ _ _ k.
6. You can also save your work in the computer's _ _ m _ r _.
7. My computer has both a hard drive and a disk _ _ _ v _.
8. Load the paper into the p _ _ n _ _ _.
9. I _ - m _ _ _ my mother every other day.
10. I'll type up my report on my _ _ m _ _ t _ _.

EXERCISE 2 *(continued)*

FUN FILL-INS

Name ________________________________

Date ________________________________

(BONUS! Continue to fill in the blanks from the word list at the top of this page.)

port	hardware	Internet
fax	software	modem
on-line	workstation	monitor
	browser	

11. Each person in my office has her or his own w _ _ _ s _ _ _ i _ _.

12. The _ _ d _ _ hooks up to my phone line.

13. A keyboard and monitor are part of a computer's _ _ r _ _ _ r _.

14. A word processing program is a kind of computer _ _ f _ _ _ r _.

15. Are you are connected to the Internet? Then you are _ n - _ _ _ _.

16. Connect the speaker cable to the _ o _ _ on the back of the computer.

17. It's hard to see what's on that tiny m _ _ _ t _ _ screen.

18. Netscape® is a _ _ _ w _ _ r. It lets you move around the World Wide Web.

19. You can send an instant letter by _ _ x.

20. The _ n _ _ r _ _ _ links computers all around the world.

EXERCISE 3

HIDDEN WORDS

Name ______________________________

Date ______________________________

Read the following story. Draw a line under each word from the list below when you first find the word in the story. Check off each word in the list as you find it. The first one is done as an example.

disk	modem	keyboard	hardware	on-line
port	laptop	printer	software	Internet
mouse	e-mail	✔computer	monitor	fax
drive	cursor	memory	workstation	browser

I work on more than one computer. When I travel, I use my laptop. At work, I have my own computer workstation. My home computer has lots of memory. It also has a color monitor and a large keyboard. I use the mouse to move the cursor around the screen. A color printer is also part of my hardware. It plugs into a port on the back of the computer. The floppy drive lets me save my work on a back-up disk. I can send a fax with the modem. My browser software lets me surf the Internet. While I'm on-line, I can also send e-mail to my friends. I use my computer a lot!

Now write each word you marked in the story on the lines below.

computer	________________	________________
________________	________________	________________
________________	________________	________________
________________	________________	________________
________________	________________	________________
________________	________________	________________
________________	________________	

EXERCISE 4
LUCKY LISTS

Name ______________________

Date ______________________

Each word in the list at the top of this page belongs in one of the categories listed below. Write each word under the category it belongs to. The first word in two columns is done as an example. Check off each word in the list as you use it.

✔disk	modem	keyboard	hardware	on-line
port	laptop	printer	software	Internet
mouse	✔e-mail	computer	monitor	fax
drive	cursor	memory	workstation	browser

Begins with a letter between *A* and *D*

disk
____
____
____
____

Begins with a letter between *E* and *J*

e-mail
____
____
____

Begins with a letter between *K* and *N*

____
____
____
____
____
____

Begins with a letter between O and *Z*

____
____
____
____
____

EXERCISE 5

PUZZLE TIME

Name ______________________________

Date ______________________________

Fill in the boxes in the puzzle with words that fit from the word list at the top of this page. Check the words off in the list as you use them. The first letter (and sometimes another letter) of each word is given. The first word is done as an example.

✔ disk	modem	keyboard	hardware	on-line
port	laptop	printer	software	Internet
mouse	e-mail	computer	monitor	fax
drive	cursor	memory	workstation	browser

BONUS! The puzzle has a secret silly sentence. It reads from the top of the puzzle down. Write the puzzle's secret silly sentence here:

____

EXERCISE 6

DAFFY DEFINITIONS

Name ______________________

Date ______________________

Choose the correct definition for each word. Circle the letter in front of the definition you choose.

1. disk
   (a) thin, flat plate that holds information
   (b) video screen that shows information
   (c) audiotape

2. port
   (a) secure area for soldiers
   (b) place where information is stored
   (c) inlet where a cable connects

3. mouse
   (a) bug that infects computers
   (b) handheld device that moves the cursor
   (c) rodent-shaped speaker

4. drive
   (a) the computer's battery
   (b) data-reading part of a computer
   (c) plug-in headphones

5. modem
   (a) device that connects to phone lines
   (b) the most up-to-date computer
   (c) a model program

6. laptop
   (a) top-of-the-line computer
   (b) portable computer
   (c) the upper part of your lap

7. e-mail
   (a) letters that come from Europe
   (b) envelopes with mail in them
   (c) electronic messages

8. cursor
   (a) small screen signal
   (b) a person who curses
   (c) curvy power cord

9. keyboard
   (a) sign outside a business
   (b) most important information
   (c) device that enters information into a computer

10. printer
    (a) memory area inside the computer
    (b) device that puts words onto paper
    (c) person who runs fast

EXERCISE 6 *(continued)*

Name ______________________________

DAFFY DEFINITIONS

Date ______________________________

(BONUS! Continue to choose the correct definition for each word.)

11. computer
    (a) machine that prints out information onto paper
    (b) machine that processes electronic information
    (c) device that cooks dinner for you

12. memory
    (a) information storage area
    (b) short note
    (c) kitchen herb

13. hardware
    (a) forks, knives, and spoons
    (b) computer program
    (c) parts of a computer system

14. monitor
    (a) person who watches a computer
    (b) computer video screen
    (c) huge and scary creature

15. workstation
    (a) work you take home
    (b) place where a train stops
    (c) desktop computer for the office

16. software
    (a) computer program
    (b) soft, squishy computer device
    (c) a monitor and printer hook-up

17. on-line
    (a) connected to the Internet
    (b) walking a fine line
    (c) writing in a straight line

18. fax
    (a) facts you find on a computer
    (b) image of a red bushy-tailed animal
    (c) document image sent over phone lines

19. browser
    (a) sleepy computer user
    (b) Internet-access software
    (c) curious mouse

20. Internet
    (a) virus-catching screen
    (b) space between the hard drive and the disk drive
    (c) worldwide computer network

EXERCISE 7

SENTENCE SENSE

Name ______________________

Date ______________________

Choose an ending that makes sense for each sentence. Circle the letter in front of the ending you choose. The vocabulary word (or words) in each sentence is underlined.

1. Insert the disk into the
   (a) drive.
   (b) monitor.
   (c) dog's mouth.
2. You'll find the monitor port
   (a) in the harbor.
   (b) on the back of the computer.
   (c) inside the keyboard.
3. To help your computer mouse run smoothly,
   (a) feed it cheese.
   (b) use it on a mouse pad.
   (c) wrap it in software.
4. A CD-ROM drive
   (a) makes the modem work.
   (b) runs your car.
   (c) reads information on disks.
5. It's handy to have a laptop when you're
   (a) away from home and office.
   (b) visiting the grandchildren.
   (c) at the top of a building.
6. Clark uses e-mail to
   (a) browse the Web.
   (b) support his local post office.
   (c) keep in touch with friends.
7. The cursor on my monitor screen
   (a) only appears at the end of a file.
   (b) is sometimes shaped like an arrow.
   (c) turns my computer on and off.
8. Bailey plugged her new modem into the
   (a) phone line.
   (b) toaster.
   (c) keyboard.
9. I can use my new color printer to make
   (a) software programs.
   (b) music.
   (c) colored pictures on paper.
10. I use my keyboard to
    (a) draw circles and squares.
    (b) create words on the screen.
    (c) read e-mails.

EXERCISE 7 *(continued)*

SENTENCE SENSE

Name ______________________________

Date ______________________________

(BONUS! Continue to choose the correct ending for each sentence.)

11. A computer lets you
    (a) get better when you're sick.
    (b) grow up.
    (c) receive and send e-mail.
12. My computer has run out of memory. Now I can't
    (a) remember how to run the computer.
    (b) save any new files.
    (c) see the computer.
13. I needed some new computer hardware. So I bought a
    (a) hammer and nails.
    (b) printer and scanner.
    (c) few new video games.
14. My favorite software program
    (a) lets me draw anything I want.
    (b) is a set of paper plates.
    (c) plugs into the modem port.
15. With a color monitor, you can
    (a) print out colorful photos.
    (b) listen to loud songs.
    (c) see colorful pictures on the screen.
16. When I'm at my workstation, I am
    (a) using my office computer.
    (b) serving lunch.
    (c) using my laptop.
17. Go on-line to
    (a) line up all your computer system cables.
    (b) hook up to the Internet.
    (c) skate in-line.
18. I sent a fax to Syd because she
    (a) had no phone.
    (b) said there was no hurry.
    (c) needed this letter right now.
19. A good browser lets you
    (a) read books quickly.
    (b) get to sleep easily.
    (c) view pages on the Internet.
20. On the Internet, I can
    (a) find information about all kinds of things.
    (b) lift weights and get fit.
    (c) be a happy intern.

EXERCISE 8

CROSSWORD CHALLENGE

Name ______________________

Date ______________________

Use the numbered clues to fill in the crossword grid. Some of the letters have been filled in already.

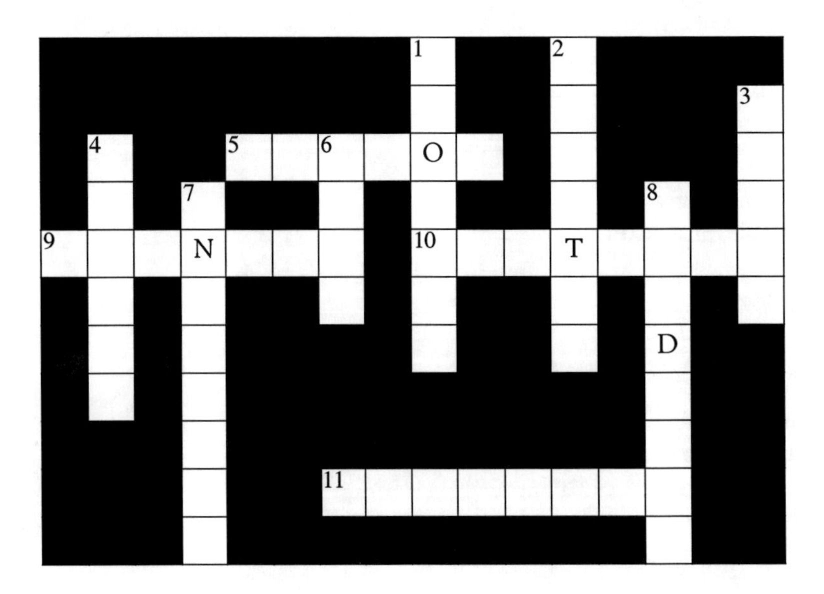

Across

5. Portable computer
9. Device that prints out files
10. Computer programs
11. Machine with a monitor and a hard drive

Down

1. Internet software
2. Video screen
3. Device that connects to phone lines
4. Small screen signal
6. Small cable inlet
7. Worldwide computer network
8. Parts of a computer system

Unit 10

EDUCATION WORDS

EXERCISE 1

WORD SENSE

Name ______________________________

Date ______________________________

Read each word below and its definition. Rewrite each word in the blanks next to its definition.

1.	example	one thing used to show what other, similar things are like	_ _ [a] _ _ _ _
2.	directions	advice or instruction on how to do something	_ _ _ _ _ _ _ _ _ [s]
3.	textbook	book used in school to study a certain subject	_ _ _ [t] _ _ _ _
4.	study	to learn by reading or thinking about something	_ _ [u] _ _
5.	graduate	to finish studying at a school and receive a diploma; also, a person who has done this	_ _ _ [d] _ _ _ _
6.	problem	question to study or solve	_ _ _ _ _ [e] _
7.	question	something asked in order to get an answer or find out something	_ _ _ _ _ _ _ [n]
8.	practice	doing something over and over again to gain skill	_ _ _ _ [t] _ _ _
9.	student	person who is going to a school or is studying something	_ _ _ _ _ [n] _
10.	college	school of higher learning, beyond high school	_ _ _ _ [e] _ _
11.	exam	a test; short for *examination*	[e] _ _ _
12.	education	process of gaining knowledge; or, the knowledge gained	_ [d] _ _ _ _ _ _ _
13.	answer	reply; solution to a problem	_ _ [s] _ _ _
14.	chapter	a main part of a book	_ _ _ _ [t] _ _
15.	homework	schoolwork you do at home, not in the classroom	_ [o] _ _ _ _ _ _
16.	research	careful study to find and learn	_ _ [s] _ _ _ _ _
17.	atlas	book of maps	_ [t] _ _ _
18.	quiz	short or informal test	_ [u] _ _
19.	dictionary	book of words arranged in order of the alphabet, with special information about each word	[d] _ _ _ _ _ _ _ _ _
20.	encyclopedia	set of books giving a lot of facts about many things	_ _ _ [y] _ _ _ _ _ _ _ _

BONUS! The boxed letters spell out a sentence. What does it say? (Write it out here if you want to:)

____

EXERCISE 2
FUN FILL-INS

Name ______________________________

Date ______________________________

Each sentence below has a word missing. Fill in each blank with a word that makes sense from the list at the top of this page. Check off each word in the list as you use it.

study	question	student
quiz	homework	practice
answer	problems	chapter
	example	

1. I spent two hours last night doing my __ o __ __ w __ __ __.
2. Maria is a good s __ __ d __ __ __. She always gets good grades.
3. Do you know the __ __ s __ __ r to that question?
4. I plan to __ t __ __ __ hard for the exam.
5. Our math test had five __ r __ __ l __ __ __ to solve.
6. An old saying is that "p __ __ __ t __ __ __ makes perfect."
7. The last __ u __ __ t __ __ __ on the test was hard to answer.
8. We had a quick __ __ i __ in class today.
9. Our teacher asked for an __ x __ __ __ l __ of a noun.
10. I now have to read c __ __ p __ __ __ two of the textbook.

EXERCISE 2 *(continued)*

FUN FILL-INS

Name ______________________________

Date ______________________________

(BONUS! Continue to fill in the blanks from the word list at the top of this page.)

college	education	graduate
exam	directions	research
atlas	dictionary	textbook
	encyclopedia	

11. I need a good grade on the final _ x _ _.

12. Raul didn't know what that word meant. So he looked it up in the d _ _ _ i _ n _ _ _.

13. Jasmine plans to _ r _ d _ _ _ _ from high school this June.

14. Then Jasmine plans to go on to _ _ _ l _ _ _.

15. The _ _ r _ _ t _ _ n _ say to circle the right answer.

16. I found the right map in the _ _ l _ _.

17. Our science _ _ x _ _ o _ _ has twenty chapters.

18. A good e _ _ c _ _ i _ _ can get you a good job.

19. You can find facts about fish in an _ n _ y _ _ _ p _ _ _ _.

20. Pete did r _ _ _ _ r _ _ to get facts for his report.

EXERCISE 3

HIDDEN WORDS

Name ____________________

Date ____________________

Read the following story. Draw a line under each word from the list below when you first find the word in the story. Check off each word in the list as you find it. The first one is done as an example.

atlas	practice	question	student	education
quiz	chapter	homework	research	directions
exam	college	problem	textbook	dictionary
✔study	answer	example	graduate	encyclopedia

I study hard to get a good education. I read each chapter of my textbook with care. I answer each practice question. I do each problem the teacher gives as homework. I make sure to follow the directions on each quiz. I do a lot of research for each report I write. I go to an encyclopedia. I look through an atlas. I use a dictionary for help while I write. I make sure I'm ready for each exam. I think I am an example of a good student. I plan to graduate this year. Then I'll attend college.

Now write each word you marked in the story on the lines below.

study	________	________
________	________	________
________	________	________
________	________	________
________	________	________
________	________	________
________	________	

EXERCISE 4
LUCKY LISTS

Name ______________________________

Date ______________________________

Each word in the list at the top of this page belongs in one of the categories listed below. Write each word under the category it belongs to. The first word in two columns is done as an example. Check off each word in the list as you use it.

✔atlas	practice	question	student	education
quiz	chapter	homework	research	directions
✔exam	college	problem	textbook	dictionary
study	answer	example	graduate	encyclopedia

Begins with a letter between *A* and *D*

atlas
____
____
____
____
____

Begins with a letter between *E* and *I*

exam
____
____
____
____
____

Begins with a letter between *J* and Q

____
____
____
____

Begins with a letter between *R* and *Z*

____
____
____
____

EXERCISE 5
PUZZLE TIME

Name ______________________________

Date ______________________________

Fill in the boxes in the puzzle with words that fit from the word list at the top of this page. Check the words off in the list as you use them. The first letter (and sometimes another letter) of each word is given. The first word is done as an example.

atlas	practice	question	student	education
quiz	chapter	homework	research	✔ directions
exam	college	problem	textbook	dictionary
study	answer	example	graduate	encyclopedia

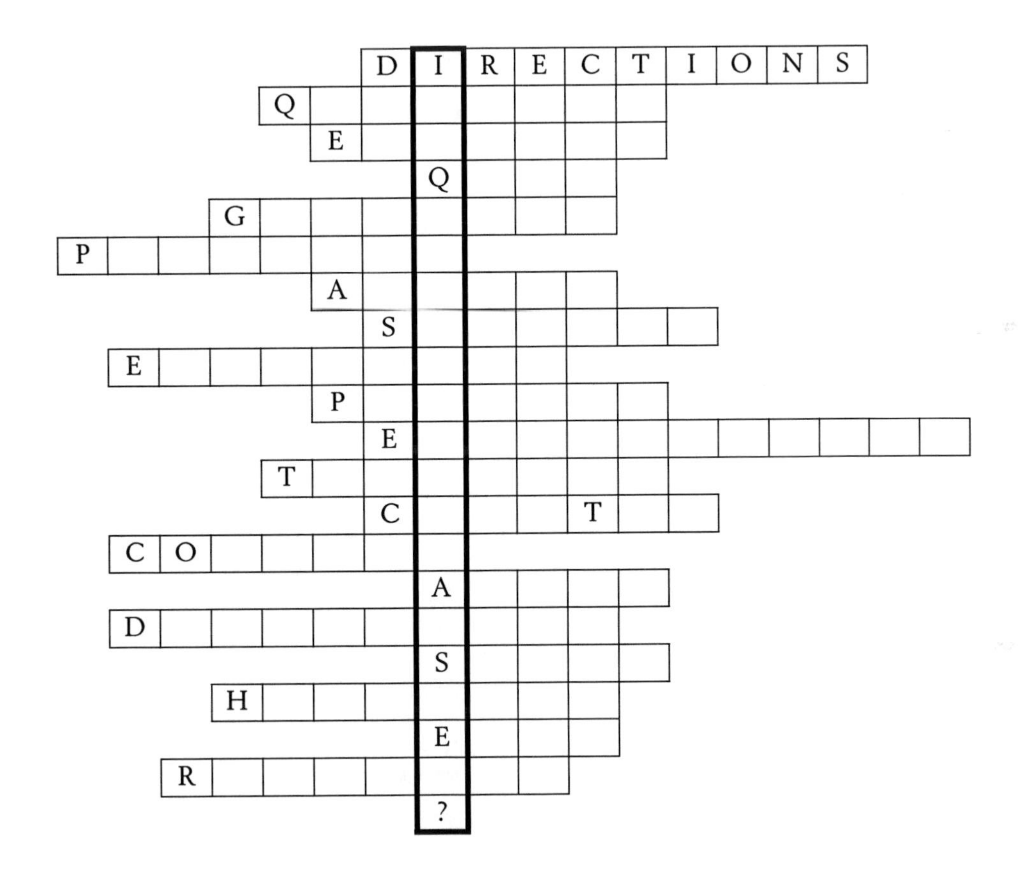

BONUS! The puzzle has a secret silly sentence. It reads from the top of the puzzle down. Write the puzzle's secret silly sentence here:

____

EXERCISE 6

DAFFY DEFINITIONS

Name ______________________________

Date ______________________________

Choose the correct definition for each word. Circle the letter in front of the definition you choose.

1. answer
   (a) odd question
   (b) reply to a question
   (c) long, drawn-out speech
2. homework
   (a) house building
   (b) cooking and cleaning
   (c) out-of-class schoolwork
3. student
   (a) dented fender
   (b) beef stew
   (c) person going to school
4. example
   (a) one thing typical of many
   (b) final exam
   (c) ex-relative
5. quiz
   (a) final test
   (b) short test
   (c) buzzing sound
6. chapter
   (a) main part of a book
   (b) balm for chapped lips
   (c) one of a two-volume set of books
7. question
   (a) search or pursuit
   (b) woman ruler
   (c) something asked
8. practice
   (a) exact amount
   (b) repeated action
   (c) magic spell
9. study
   (a) strong and hardy
   (b) learn about a thing
   (c) push away
10. problem
    (a) thing to study or solve
    (b) test answer
    (c) time out of jail

EXERCISE 6 *(continued)*

DAFFY DEFINITIONS

Name ______________________________

Date ______________________________

(BONUS! Continue to choose the correct definition for each word.)

11. directions
    (a) how-to advice
    (b) amusements
    (c) reference books about words

12. college
    (a) school for children
    (b) school of higher learning
    (c) pasted-together picture

13. atlas
    (a) book of word meanings
    (b) book of maps
    (c) globe

14. research
    (a) careful study
    (b) search and rescue mission
    (c) stretching exercise

15. education
    (a) holiday from school
    (b) lack of knowledge
    (c) gaining of knowledge

16. textbook
    (a) picture book
    (b) school book
    (c) cooking book

17. dictionary
    (a) set of books filled with facts
    (b) drawing game
    (c) book of word meanings

18. exam
    (a) test
    (b) short quiz
    (c) sleeping pill

19. graduate
    (a) drop out of school
    (b) stop something gradually
    (c) finish a course of study

20. encyclopedia
    (a) work of fiction
    (b) set of fact books
    (c) violent storm

EXERCISE 7
SENTENCE SENSE

Name ______________________________

Date ______________________________

Choose an ending that makes sense for each sentence. Circle the letter in front of the ending you choose. The vocabulary word (or words) in each sentence is underlined.

1. I <u>study</u> a lot so I can
   (a) get good grades.
   (b) grow taller and stronger.
   (c) become stupid.
2. Today's <u>quiz</u> was
   (a) hungry and thirsty.
   (b) long and involved.
   (c) short and quick.
3. At last, Selena gave her <u>answer</u> to Brad's
   (a) motor scooter.
   (b) question.
   (c) sneeze.
4. I do my <u>homework</u>
   (a) under my arms.
   (b) while I'm asleep.
   (c) at my desk.
5. To figure out the answer to the <u>problem</u>, Yana
   (a) used her calculator.
   (b) ate the dinner roll.
   (c) stopped thinking.
6. As an <u>example</u> of fruit, Paul showed
   (a) an orange.
   (b) a crying baby.
   (c) his report card.
7. Every <u>student</u> at our school
   (a) is a school bus.
   (b) does not study.
   (c) wears a uniform.
8. The <u>practice</u> games help us
   (a) forget the rules.
   (b) be better players.
   (c) get worse and worse at the game.
9. The first few <u>chapters</u> of the novel
   (a) finish the story.
   (b) get the story started.
   (c) tell the whole story.
10. When I ask a <u>question</u>, I expect
   (a) a hot dog.
   (b) an airplane ride.
   (c) an answer.

EXERCISE 7 *(continued)*

SENTENCE SENSE

Name ______________________________

Date ______________________________

(BONUS! Continue to choose the correct ending for each sentence.)

11. The local college is full of
    (a) young child students.
    (b) collies.
    (c) adult students.
12. Our final exam
    (a) counted for half our grade.
    (b) was a counter-spy.
    (c) sighed and moaned.
13. Our great new atlas is full of
    (a) shirts.
    (b) maps.
    (c) wizards.
14. When I finished my education, I
    (a) knew a lot.
    (b) felt very ignorant.
    (c) knew I had eaten too much.
15. If you follow directions, you will
    (a) be very sorry.
    (b) get fat and ill.
    (c) do things the right way.
16. Jason used his dictionary to
    (a) give himself a massage.
    (b) find out how to spell that word.
    (c) fill the refrigerator.
17. A college graduate
    (a) is sent to jail.
    (b) can get better jobs.
    (c) is the school's gym.
18. Hallie did research on the Internet to
    (a) feed her dog.
    (b) waste her time.
    (c) get the facts.
19. The science textbook
    (a) gives all the basic facts for the course.
    (b) makes a warm shelter.
    (c) has good pictures but no words.
20. My CD-ROM encyclopedia is full of
    (a) snack foods.
    (b) violent action games.
    (c) fascinating fun facts.

EXERCISE 8
CROSSWORD CHALLENGE

Name ____________________

Date ____________________

Use the numbered clues to fill in the crossword grid. Some of the letters have been filled in already.

Across

4. School of higher learning
5. A test
8. Person who goes to a school
9. School lesson you do outside school

Down

1. A main part of a book
2. Question to study or solve
3. Something asked
6. Reply to a question
7. Book of maps

Share Your Bright Ideas with Us!

We want to hear from you! Your valuable comments and suggestions will help us meet your current and future classroom needs.

Your name____Date______________________

School name____

School address____

City ________________________State _____Zip__________Phone number (_________)______________

Grade level taught________Subject area(s) taught__________________________Average class size______

Where did you purchase this publication?____

Was your salesperson knowledgeable about this product? Yes_____ No_____

What monies were used to purchase this product?

___School supplemental budget ___Federal/state funding ___Personal

Please "grade" this Walch publication according to the following criteria:

Quality of service you received when purchasing .... A B C D F
Ease of use .... A B C D F
Quality of content .... A B C D F
Page layout .... A B C D F
Organization of material .... A B C D F
Suitability for grade level .... A B C D F
Instructional value .... A B C D F

COMMENTS:____

____

What specific supplemental materials would help you meet your current—or future—instructional needs?

____

Have you used other Walch publications? If so, which ones?___________________________________

May we use your comments in upcoming communications? ___Yes ___No

Please **FAX** this completed form to **207-772-3105**, or mail it to:

Product Development, J. Weston Walch, Publisher, P. O. Box 658, Portland, ME 04104-0658

We will send you a **FREE GIFT** as our way of thanking you for your feedback. **THANK YOU!**